MW00628316

Country Living

The Ultimate Guide to Homesteading, Beekeeping, Raising Livestock, and Achieving Self-Sufficiency in the Countryside

© Copyright 2023 - All rights reserved.

The content contained within this book may not be reproduced, duplicated, or transmitted without direct written permission from the author or the publisher.

Under no circumstances will any blame or legal responsibility be held against the publisher or author for any damages, reparation, or monetary loss due to the information contained within this book, either directly or indirectly.

Legal Notice:

This book is copyright-protected. It is only for personal use. You cannot amend, distribute, sell, use, quote, or paraphrase any part of the content within this book without the consent of the author or publisher.

Disclaimer Notice:

Please note the information contained within this document is for educational and entertainment purposes only. All effort has been executed to present accurate, up-to-date, reliable, and complete information. No warranties of any kind are declared or implied. Readers acknowledge that the author is not engaging in the rendering of legal, financial, medical, or professional advice. The content within this book has been derived from various sources. Please consult a licensed professional before attempting any techniques outlined in this book.

By reading this document, the reader agrees that under no circumstances is the author responsible for any losses, direct or indirect, that are incurred as a result of the use of the information contained within this document, including, but not limited to, errors, omissions, or inaccuracies.

Table of Contents

Introduction

Country living . . . Homesteading. What images do these terms conjure up in your mind? "Little House on the Prairie" (for those old enough to remember it)? Low-slung farmhouses built of timber, surrounded by fields full of crops and livestock? You wouldn't be too far off the mark, but the reality of homesteading is a little less glamorous, although no less rewarding.

It's fair to say that homesteading isn't for the faint-hearted, nor is it for those who think it's an easy life and aren't prepared to put in the effort to make it work. It offers you a way to live your life free of the shackles of society, with little reliance on public utilities, and a way to produce your own food and many other things you rely on in your current life. It is hard work, but your effort will pay dividends in the long run.

If you aren't sure where to start or what to do, you've chosen the right book. It will lay out for you every step you need to take, everything you need to consider, and tips on making it all the success you dreamed it would be. This is written in plain English, with no hard-to-understand terms, plenty of images, and step-by-step instructions to help you along the way.

If you've dreamed of living a homestead life, settle in and read. By the end of this book, you will know everything you've ever wanted to know, and a bit more besides – and you'll know if this is the way of life for you or not.

Part One: Setting Up Your Homestead

Chapter 1: Planning Your Homestead

Homesteads mean something different to everyone you speak to, but broadly speaking, it's about living self-sufficiently. Most people consider the most essential parts to be the land, the buildings on it, and farming to be self-sufficient, at least partly, if not totally.

So, what do you need to consider?

Location

Choosing your land and its location is the first place to start.
https://unsplash.com/photos/person-holding-red-round-medication-pill-Z8UgB80_46w

The obvious place to begin is the land, its location, and several other factors that you need to consider, and it all comes down to what you want.

Space and Size:

What size of land you want depends on what you want to do with it, but some things you need to consider are:

- **Your Family:** You need enough space for everyone joining you on your journey, so your land must be big enough for a big enough house.
- **Livestock:** How many animals are you planning to keep? You may want to start small, but remember, you need room to expand, too. Make sure you have enough land for housing and grazing.
- **Crops:** You need enough space to plant, harvest, and store your crops, as well as rotate your crop areas.

Also, think about the maintenance. The larger the land, the more maintenance it takes, so ensure you understand the time and resources needed.

What Are You Using the Land For?

Is it going to be residential, agriculture, or a mixture? Are you living in an RV or intending to build a home? Will you live there all year round?

You must ensure your land is zoned for what you intend to use it for. For example, if you want to build a house, it must have residential zoning. When you understand how much space you require, you will find it easier to locate the right piece of land.

Where It Is:

This is one of the more important factors, and there are two things in particular you need to consider:

Accessibility: How easy is it to get to the land? If it will be a full-time home, you need easy access all year round, regardless of the weather. Some factors to consider include:

- Is it near to major highways and roads?
- What condition is the access road in?
- How near is the closest city or town?

If you don't live there full time, you can compromise here, but poor access can make it harder to sell the property in the future.

How Close Are Amenities?

This is also an important consideration, but it depends on what your goals are and if you have dependents. The amenities you might want to be close to include:

- Hospitals
- Doctors
- Schools
- Grocery stores
- Veterinarian
- Farm supply store
- Hardware store

That said, if getting away from everything is your goal, you might want somewhere more isolated. However, the further you are from the amenities, the more difficult it will be to get to them should you need them.

Land Characteristics

Aside from location, you must also consider certain aspects of the land.

Topography:

This is about the physical features, such as slopes, elevation, drainage, etc. These all affect your success, or otherwise, in raising livestock and growing food, not to mention building your house and other buildings. Too steep, and you could struggle to build or to grow crops. If the land floods in places, you may struggle to raise certain livestock or grow crops.

Conversely, it could be the ideal spot if it is well-drained with little to no slope. Terracing is one way of growing crops on gently sloping land, and you won't have to worry about flooding if the soil is well-drained.

Soil Quality:

Soil quality has a considerable effect on livestock and crop health. You need fertile, deep, well-drained soil to allow your crop roots to grow strong. It should be full of the nutrients your plants need, and it must be well-drained so it doesn't flood or become waterlogged.

If possible, get the soil pH and nutrient levels tested. That way, you will know what grows and what doesn't or what you need to do to amend the soil quality.

Legal and Zoning

These are critical considerations as they can affect how you use and develop the land. The two crucial issues are:

Zoning Restrictions:

These regulate how you can use and develop land in certain areas. Before you buy any land, you must find out the zoning laws for the region/state to make sure you can legally homestead on it and build what you need. You can speak to the local zoning department, who will explain the local laws and restrictions. You may also want to talk to a real-estate lawyer to ensure you understand everything fully.

Title Deeds/Ownership:

You must ensure the sellers actually own the title and that no one else has a claim or lien on the land. Get a copy of the title deed and ask a real estate attorney to look at it. They will tell you if any issues could stop you from owning the land.

You may also need to consider title insurance that protects you should any legal issues or claims arise after the purchase. Yes, it is more money, but it is well worth the cost.

Financial Considerations

The financial aspects are perhaps some of the most important, and there are two you need to consider:

Budgeting:

You must plan your budget to determine your spending limits.
https://unsplash.com/photos/a-person-holding-a-bunch-of-money-in-their-hand-9uCmnwC2KR4?utm_content=creditShareLink&utm_medium=referral&utm_source=unsplash

You must set out a budget before you even think about looking for a piece of land. Determine your maximum spending limits on the land, then calculate the costs of property taxes, closing costs, and insurance.

If your chosen land doesn't already have a house, you need to consider the building costs, whether you do it yourself or hire contractors. If it does have a house on it, consider the costs of potential renovations.

If you intend to finance your purchase, consider that some lenders want a bigger down payment than they would for a house. The interest rates may be higher and repayment terms shorter, too. You need to choose the option that fits your circumstances and budget.

Resale Value Potential:

Obviously, this won't be the first thing on your mind, but you may need to consider it in the future. Try to buy in areas with strong demand, as this can increase future prices. Think about:

- Location
- Zoning laws
- Natural resources

These are all important when considering resale value, and unique features, such as lovely views or water access, can boost the value significantly.

Environmental Factors

Environmental factors can get in the way of your ability to work and live, and there are two that you need to consider in particular:

Climate:

Climate affects whether you can raise livestock or grow crops. Some are more suited to specific climates, so research to ensure you can raise the food you intend to raise in that particular climate. Extreme weather also affects things, so if the region is prone to hurricanes, severe flooding, and droughts, not to mention wildfires, you may need to rethink your choice. Some factors to consider are:

- Average temperatures
- Rain/snowfall levels
- How long the growing season is
- Soil type and quality

- Topography
- Elevation
- Microclimates

Disaster Risks:

Natural disasters are bad enough anywhere, but they can significantly threaten a homestead. Consider the disaster risks in the region, as some places are more prone than others. Research the area's history to assess the disaster risk, looking for the following:

- Earthquakes
- Floods
- Hurricanes
- Landslides
- Tornadoes
- Wildfires

You must also consider man-made disasters like chemical spills and industrial accidents. Again, research, look at historical data, and speak to emergency management agencies in the area.

Infrastructure and Utilities

When you purchase land to build a homestead, you must consider the available utilities and infrastructure.

Electricity and Water:

These are critical to a homestead, so think about the following:

- **Water:** Does the land have a reliable water source? A stream, river, or well? If not, how do you gain access to water? Is the water drinkable? Can it be safely used for crops and livestock? You may need to factor in the cost of water tests.
- **Electricity:** Does the land have electricity access? If not, what option do you have? Can you use wind or solar?

Waste Management

Waste management is one of the most critical aspects of keeping your homestead sustainable and healthy. Think about the following:

- **Septic System:** Is the land connected to the municipal sewer system? If not, can you install a septic system? Consider the cost in your calculations and whether the land is suitable for the installation.

- **Composting:** This is one of the best ways of managing organic waste, so consider if the resources and space are available for a good composting system.
- **Trash Disposal:** Is the land on the municipal trash pickup service? Are you near a recycling plant? You must consider how you will dispose of non-organic waste and consider the cost involved.

Only when you consider all of these aspects can you begin to ensure that your homestead has everything you need to be successful.

Designing Your Homestead

Planning your homestead means ensuring all space can be used effectively, and the right design will mean you don't have to waste time and money redesigning it later. The best time to start is the fall, as the warmer season is ending, and you can get your homestead and gardening areas set up.

First, measure your space and draw it out. Add in all the structures on the land, including measurements, so you know what you can work with. Your drawing doesn't need to be perfect, but it does need to be accurate.

Next, check your local regulations, especially if you want to keep bees or livestock, including respecting the distance from the property lines the law demands.

Determine what you want. Are you after a fruit orchard? Bees? Chickens and ducks? Or something larger, like cattle and horses? Do you need an area for your pets or children? List everything and then work out where it will go on your plan.

Planning Your Layout

Make sure the must-haves are mapped on your design layout first. For example, if you really need a vegetable garden, head out into your land and measure the light and shade at various times during the day. A veggie garden needs maximum sunlight and well-drained, fertile soil. If you live in the north, you should choose an area with the most sun. Conversely, in the south, choose an area that gets shade in the afternoon. Bear in mind that buildings may provide shade.

Make sure bees and livestock are positioned as per regulations. If there aren't any, put them where it suits you, but keep in mind the suitability of the land for the purpose intended. Play around with several layout ideas until you get the one that works for you.

Layout Plans

If you have a suburban plot and are finding it hard to plan your homestead, here are a few ideas to help you.

Large Suburban Plots: these days, if you have a large plot, you likely have a large house but very little land. However, that doesn't mean you can't build a homestead. Careful planning ensures you can fit in a veggie gardening area, be it raised beds, vertical planting or containers, a couple of beehives, or a few chickens, and still have space for your kids to play. Use all the land around the house to full capacity, bearing in mind the laws about distances from neighboring plots.

Medium Suburban Plot: having more space in the backyard means having more space to be self-sufficient, and you can use the front yard, too. Some ideas include:

- A fruit-tree guild in the front yard
- An area for composting
- Beehives
- Small livestock, i.e., chickens and rabbits
- Keyhole garden bed
- Greenhouse
- Small pond

Small Suburban Plot: perhaps you live in a duplex and don't have as much space as you would like, but you can still use raised beds and containers. Some ideas include:

- A perennial veggie bed
- Chicken tractor/mobile coop
- Rabbit hutch with run
- Patio planters

Of course, if you have an acre or more, you can do all this in a much-scaled-up version. It all comes down to using your space in the most effective way possible while respecting local planning laws.

Homestead Planning Tips

Here are a few tips to help you in your planning:

- **Use What's Already There.** If your land has established trees, gather up the dead leaves and make compost, or use them as part of a food forest. If there's a pond, add edible perennials.
- **Study Building Designs.** Work out what will work regarding beehives, hutches, pens, coops, and greenhouses. Use existing buildings where possible and renovate them to meet your needs.
- **Maximize Your Space.** If you are short on space, use trellises and fences for vertical planting, and consider raised beds and keyhole gardens to grow more food in a small space.

Building Your Homestead

You may find it cheaper to build your own home, especially if you can't afford to buy land with a home already on it. The cost of property is very high now, and more people are choosing to build their own, especially when starting a homestead.

Building your own home means building it how you want it, not having to put up with or renovating what's already there. Things to consider are:

Building Materials:

There are plenty of cost-effective building materials that can help you save money and time:

- **Prefab Panels:** These are usually made from concrete, steel, or wood, made off-site, and shipped for assembly. These take less time to build, which means less cost, fewer workers, and less skill. They are often considered eco-friendly because there is less waste, and prefab homes are energy efficient because of their enclosed design.
- **Precast Concrete:** Precast concrete panels are much cheaper than building with concrete and offer insulation, fireproofing, and security.
- **Shipping Containers:** One of the more popular home choices these days, shipping containers are eco-friendly as you are recycling an existing container. Already constructed with a roof,

walls, and a frame, these can save money on materials and labor, and it's much quicker to put a home together.

- **Reclaimed Wood:** This is often repurposed from wooden structures, such as boats, shipping crates, and old barns. They are eco-friendly because you aren't cutting down trees for fresh wood. They are also cost-effective and give your home a unique look.

- **Bamboo:** Bamboo is fast-growing and cheaper than wood. It is versatile and sustainable and can be used for roofing, framing, flooring, and fencing. It is also considered stronger than steel.

- **Bricks:** One of the highest-end materials you can use, bricks are also cost-effective, depending on the type you use. Solid bricks are expensive, but building a wood frame and a freestanding brick wall is much cheaper. However, it can be labor intensive, and using a contractor will significantly increase costs, too.

- **Cob:** A natural material made from sand, clay, straw, or another organic, fibrous material, cob is one of the cheapest and most flexible building materials. You can even use it to make bricks and stack them, creating a good foundation to build on.

- **Eco Bricks:** These are made from plastic bottles filled with plastic waste, reducing plastic and pollution in the biosphere and creating a much cheaper building material.

Other things you can do to keep construction costs down include:

- **Easy Shapes:** Don't make your home layout complicated. Keep things simple with squares and rectangles to keep your costs down. If you want a bigger home, go up rather than out – it's still cheaper. You can apply this to the roof, too. The simpler the design, the cheaper the cost.

- **DIY:** If you have construction experience, this can be cheaper than hiring contractors for the whole job, but you must have the right knowledge, skilled labor, and materials.

- **Energy-Efficiency:** Building an eco-efficient home saves pollution and significantly reduces your energy bills.

- **No Expensive Finishes:** These can wait until you've saved up more money. A solid, secure home is more important at this stage.

- **Group Water Storage:** Try to plan so your water requirements are near to each other, such as your bathroom, kitchen, laundry room, etc. This reduces the need for more plumbing materials and can keep your costs down.

Chapter 2: Sustainable Living Considerations

One of the most important parts of homesteading is being self-sufficient, which means managing your water and energy supplies. You also need to consider reducing your carbon footprint, and you can do that in several ways. This chapter will look at water and alternative energy before moving on to recycling and waste disposal.

Water

Water is critical to everyone, and you'll need it for drinking, cleaning, cooking, bathing, and irrigating your land. Having a reliable source is essential, so here are some ways you can learn to manage your water if you are not on a main supply.

Rainwater Harvesting

Rainwater harvesting allows you to store rainwater for later use.
https://unsplash.com/photos/black-round-metal-tank-on-brown-wooden-table-L7Ps6-zLDpI

This is when you collect rainwater and store it for the many uses you'll need it for. It is one of the most eco-friendly and sustainable practices and is incredibly helpful for homesteaders as it gives them a free water source.

You can do this in several ways, but the more common method is by using gutters, cisterns, or rain barrels to collect water from the roof. Rain barrels come in all sizes, from 50 gallons up, and cisterns are much larger, capable of storing thousands of gallons.

When you set your system up, here are some aspects you should take into consideration:

- Roof type and size
- Amount of rain
- Intended use

The best roof materials are tiles, metal, or asphalt, while asbestos, cedar shakes, and other similar materials come with a contamination risk.

You can use rainwater for cooking, drinking (it must be filtered and treated), irrigation, and cleaning. As it is naturally soft, there are no chemicals or chlorine, so it's ideal for everything.

Wells

If you have a good well on your property, that's great. They are consistent and reliable, tapping into water beneath the ground and supplying a constant source for all your needs.

Wells come in all types, including dug, drilled, and driven. Drilled wells are the most common but require a drilling rig, while dug wells mean getting the digging tools out. A pipe is driven into the ground for a driven well.

Various factors affect depth and yield, including geology, well type, and water table. If building your own, employ a hydrogeologist or professional driller to determine the well location and maximum depth and to ensure it is within your local regulations and follows safety standards.

Getting a continuous supply of water means regular maintenance is required. That includes:

- Water quality tests
- Structure inspections
- Pressure and pump maintenance
- Cleaning the surroundings

Water Conservation

Another important part of homesteading is water conversation. When your resources are limited, using what you have efficiently is critical:

- Mulch your garden to keep moisture in
- Go for drought-tolerant plants
- Use drip irrigation/soaker hoses
- Collect greywater (showers, sinks, dishwashing, laundry) and reuse it in the garden
- Make sure you have no leaks
- Use low-flow faucets/toilets/shower heads to reduce usage

- Use rainwater harvesting systems
- Don't over-water gardens, and only water during cooler hours

Alternative Energy Sources

When you start a homestead, you can use alternative energy sources. One of the biggest reasons for the popularity of alternative sources is that they are eco-friendly, but they also offer a cheaper alternative to mains energy. Here are some of the main sources:

- **Wood Fuel:** Used for heating and/or cooking, wood fuel is incredibly cost-effective compared to electric or gas. While trees take a long time to regrow, wood is sustainable and renewable, and if your land has plenty of trees, you have a great ready-made source.

- **Solar:** Solar is one of the most popular alternative sources, and if done right, you can generate more than enough power for all your appliances. You can mount panels on your roof or set them up on your land somewhere. However, hiring a specialist to install the system is best unless you are experienced, as your panels must connect to your existing wiring. You could also consider a battery storage system to give you constant electricity. If you live in the north, you may want to consider using solar with other alternative sources, as you may not get enough sun to power the system.

- **Wind:** The next most popular wind generation requires wind turbines, which can be noisy. They offer a clean energy source, but you need to live in a region with steady winds. You can also have a battery system to store excess energy. You must check your local regulations, though, as not all areas allow wind turbines, and there will likely be regulations about placement.

- **Water:** Hydropower works 24 hours daily, provided you have the proper setup. A small stream won't cut it. If that's all you have, you'll need to tie it in with other sources.

- **Methane:** A relatively new option, methane is fast becoming popular among homesteaders, particularly those with large numbers of manure-producing livestock. Simply put, it uses gases produced by organic matter as it rots to produce fuel. You can also produce methane with composted plant materials, and it's pretty easy to set up.

Waste Reduction and Recycling

Recycling and waste reduction are hot topics right now, and homesteading is the perfect place to give it a go. Even if your land is on a trash collection route, you still want to consider reducing the amount of waste and reusing/recycling where possible. Here are some ways to help you get started:

Paper/Cardboard

There are so many ways to reuse paper and cardboard that throwing it away is senseless. You can use it in the following ways:

- Reuse toilet roll tubes and egg carts as biodegradable seed starters
- Cut up used printer paper to make notepads
- Weave packing paper (Amazon, etc.) into baskets
- Reuse old wrapping paper as photo matting
- Use newspapers in the garden as mulch. Tear it up and layer it around your plants, and it will eventually rot down, feeding the soil.
- Shred paper to use as chicken bedding
- Chuck it in the compost bin
- Use it to start your wood fire

Plastic

Everything is made of plastic these days, and it's one of the worst materials as it doesn't biodegrade. However, it does break down into small pieces, causing damage and death to wildlife. Here's how to reuse plastics on your homestead or reduce your usage altogether:

- Reuse plastic shopping bags as pillow stuffing
- Use large plastic bottles as mini greenhouses in the garden
- Ziploc bags can be reused many times
- Instead of plastic shopping bags, buy reusable ones
- Buy drinks in reusable bottles
- Don't use disposable straws and cups. Buy/use reusable ones instead

Glass

Glass is one of the easiest materials to reuse and is environmentally friendly.

- Turn glass bottles into planters.
- Reuse glass jars and bottles as storage vessels, especially when you buy things like flour, sugar, beans, etc., in bulk.
- Reuse broken glass as decorations on the wall or in art projects.

Food Waste

One of the best ways to reuse or recycle is to compost what you can. That applies to food waste, as a composter can turn it into a fantastic fertilizer. Composting breaks materials down into nutrient-rich compost, reducing reliance on landfills and fossil fuels and reducing emissions.

There are a few types of composting to consider:

- Aerated (turned) windrow composting
- Aerated static pile composting
- In-vessel composting
- On-site composting
- Vermicomposting

Which one you use will depend on your climate, homestead size, use, and how much compost you need. You could even run two or three systems separately. You can make a composting bin by using a large bin with holes in it or building one outdoors out of old pallets and wire netting. Alternatively, buy a purpose-made one.

How to Reduce Your Carbon Footprint

When you start a homestead, there's every chance you want to try living off the land, which is great for your finances and the environment. When you rely less on external entities, you get more control over your interaction with your land, and you may even be looking for more ways to reduce your carbon footprint. Here are some for you to consider:

1. **Make Your Own Clothes or Buy Second-Hand:** While it may be fun to have new clothes, it takes numerous resources to make them. For example, cotton is incredibly water-intensive, while man-made fibers use coal-based methods to make them. Save money by buying clothes from second-hand stores, buying material and making your own, or altering your clothes.

2. **Compost Food Waste:** As mentioned above, composting is low-emission, creating wonderful compost and fertilizer for your veggie garden. Make piles of organic waste, such as plant material, leaves, and food scraps, interspersed with layers of paper and cardboard.

3. **Use Renewable Energy:** Moving off the grid is a great way to reduce your carbon footprint. Think about using any of the renewable sources mentioned in the earlier section. You could also consider purchasing a solar generator to start with to see how you get on before you go full solar or use wind turbines if your land is suitable.

4. **Grow Your Own Food:** Raising livestock and growing fruit and vegetables is a great way to reduce your reliance on mass-produced foods at the grocery store, with the benefit that you know exactly what has gone into your food. By producing your own, you are not contributing to the fuel pollution to deliver your foods to the markets, not purchasing inorganic foods smothered in chemicals and full of growth hormones, and there is no waste, either. You could consider joining a farmer's community, where you can exchange foods or purchase organic.

5. **Recycle and Reuse:** Wherever possible, reuse or recycle everything. If you have paper or cardboard that you can't use in another way, chuck it in the compost bin. Reuse egg cartons as plant starters, reuse glass jars and bottles for storage, and so on.

6. **Collect Water:** Set up rainwater systems to collect water you can use around your property. You can use it just for watering the garden or go the whole hog and set up a whole-home system.

Just a few simple steps can help reduce your carbon footprint significantly, and you'll learn some interesting uses for things you never thought of. At the end of the day, everyone has to do their bit to help save the planet, and even the smallest things can help.

Chapter 3: Should You Go Off-Grid?

Going off-grid means not relying on any public utilities or the rest of society for your everyday living. It involves being self-sufficient to the extent that your energy is supplied by renewable means, you have your own water source, and you grow and raise all your own food.

At one time, living off-grid meant living in a remote rural area, well away from everyone and everything. These days, you can live anywhere and be off-grid, at least partly, but if that's what you want to do, there are some things you must consider.

First, decide where you want to live. The best place would be a large plot of land with a water supply, preferably running water but not a main supply. You'll need some kind of water collection system, too.

Vegetable gardens are a necessity when it comes to living off-grid.
https://unsplash.com/fr/photos/plante-verte-et-rouge-sur-cloture-en-bois-blanc-hvSBya7hX2Q

You'll need enough land to create a decent vegetable garden, have fruit trees and bushes, and raise a certain amount of livestock for food.

In terms of power, you'll need to decide on solar, methane, wind turbine, or some other renewable source, but factor the costs of the system into your budget. You'll also need to consider a battery storage system if you choose wind or solar. Otherwise, you'll only have power during daylight hours.

Lastly, you need to consider a waste disposal/septic system and add the costs to your budget.

Sustainability of Off-Grid Living

Off-grid living is more sustainable than relying on standard means of energy, water, and food supplies, partly because you won't use as much energy but mostly because off-grid systems are renewable.

20% of greenhouse gas emissions come from powering, cooling, and heating homes, just in the USA. When you live off-grid, you do your bit for climate change by not adding to those emissions. On top of that, off-grid homes typically have better insulation, don't use so much energy, and use renewable energy sources instead of fossil fuels.

You no longer rely on grocery stores because you grow and produce your food, including eggs, milk, meat, and vegetables. You no longer consume anything that is not organic and no longer eat chemical-laden foods wrapped in plastic and transported, sometimes a long way. And if you have your own compost heap, you save water and soil and reduce your wastage.

Pros and Cons

Off-grid living comes with advantages and disadvantages.

Pros:

- **You Save Money.** The upfront costs of setting up can be expensive, but your costs go down after the initial investment. Your energy bills are cheaper, and you purchase less food as you grow your own.

- **Connection with Nature.** When you live on a large piece of land, you get to immerse yourself in nature and escape modern life and all the stresses it brings. It's long since been recognized that just 2 hours a week spent outdoors in nature significantly improves mental and physical health. Off-grid living means being surrounded by nature 24/7.

- **Sustainable and Self-Sufficient Lifestyle.** By choosing renewable energy and growing your own food, you learn to rely on yourself and not contribute anywhere near as much to society's throwaway culture.

While off-grid living is rewarding, it can also be incredibly challenging, not to mention requiring commitment.

Cons:

- **Substantial Investment.** Setting up an off-grid homestead is not cheap, as you have to consider land purchase, licenses, permits, building costs, water supply, renewable energy, and waste disposal systems.

- **Hard Work.** You definitely need some skills, or you need the money to hire people who know what they are doing to set up your energy and water systems. You also need to know how to raise livestock, possibly butcher it yourself, and learn how to grow vegetables and turn everything into food to survive.

- **Things Can Go Wrong.** Nothing ever goes smoothly, and you must expect things to go wrong, such as your water or power supply failing at times.

- **It Can Be Isolating.** If you choose to buy a piece of land in the middle of nowhere, be aware that you may be quite isolated and not see another person for days, weeks, or even months unless you head into the nearest town or city. Ask yourself if that's what you really want.

Chapter 4: Building Your Homestead

When you've purchased your land and are ready to begin your new life, the first thing you need is a roof over your head. No doubt you've been told you should spend a year on your land before you build a home, but most people don't fancy camping for that long.

Few homesteaders have the necessary experience or skills to design or build a home, but the problem is likely because you're thinking too big. Your first home doesn't have to be massive. Think small. Think simple to start with because you can always expand later on. All you need are a few basic necessities to get you going.

First, you need a source of running water, be it a well, mains, or a spring. Secondly, you need a power source of some kind. Once you've got that, you can plan out a basic home that will serve your purpose until you can expand into something more luxurious.

The Bare Necessities

Here are the essential things you need in your house:

1. Somewhere to Sleep

A sofa bed can serve as a bed at night and a sofa during the day.

https://unsplash.com/photos/white-bed-linen-near-window-tGo2ngNyKyM?utm_content=creditShareLink&utm_medium=referral&utm_source=unsplash

While having a room specifically for sleeping, if there's only you/your partner, a comfy bed tucked away or a sofa bed will suffice. Provided you've got decent warm bedding, you'll be just fine. You can even use a bed as a sofa during the day by switching pillows for cushions. If you need a bit of privacy, a curtain rod and curtains will work.

2. Somewhere to Store and Make Food

Again, having a separate kitchen is nice, but it isn't necessary to start with. All you need is somewhere flat and solid to work on near your stove. A solid table will work, or a solid board on heavy brackets. You should invest in some kitchen cabinets, too. They don't have to be new ones, either. Pick up some old ones and upcycle them. A couple of shelves above the worktop and a basic sink, and you're all set. You can drain the kitchen sink into a container outside and use it to water your garden. You also need a couple of basic baking dishes, crockery, and cutlery, and for closed storage, a few kitchen cabinets stacked up will work well.

3. Heating and Cooking

You will need some kind of stove, but if power is an issue, use a wood stove or propane gas. A wood stove will also provide heating. If you do have power, invest in a microwave, crockpot, toaster, kettle, and a basic two-ring hob. That will get you started, and you'll at least be able to cook something.

4. Somewhere to Store Your Clothes

If you are switching city life for a homestead, there's a good chance you've downsized your wardrobe to just the bare essentials. Use storage bins or drawers beneath the bed if you don't need to hang anything up. If not, get a chest of drawers. Again, think second-hand that you can upcycle. This will also double as a sideboard and not take up much floor space.

5. Bathing and Toilet

If you live somewhere with warm weather all year, an outdoor shower and outhouse will do the trick. However, if your region gets cold, you'll want somewhere indoors and a little warmer. It doesn't have to be big, just enough for a basic toilet (think sawdust or compost for now) and a washstand, and it can double as a wet room for a basic shower. Again, link the drain to water storage outside so you can reuse the water.

6. Somewhere to Store Your Tools and Work

You'll need tools for your homestead, so you'll need somewhere to store them. Add a toolshed onto the side of your house and give it an entrance from the outside and one into the house. Make sure it is secure. If you have space, add a covered workspace, too. This will keep you cool in warm weather and sheltered from the elements in cold weather. You can also use it to hang your washing out and hang the washing out. Don't be mean with the space. Ensure it is at least 8 feet wide and as long as needed so you have space to work.

Let's Get Building

Those are what you need as a minimum, so get drawing and plan your house. The rest of this chapter will give you some building instructions and help you get your first shelter built. The building instructions will be much the same for most plans. You will now learn how to build a deck on posts and add walls with conventional framing between each post. Those posts provide support for the roof rafters.

Step One:

a. Mark out your building plan on the ground. You can use string and poles to do this, ensuring you mark the position of the corners and every post going into the construction.

b. Dig the post holes deep enough that they go beneath the frost line or until you hit a big rock. If the rock isn't deep enough in the ground, you may need to rethink the position. Three feet is usually deep enough to support a 4 x 4, 14-foot post.

Step Two:

a. Set your posts in place and concrete them in. Make sure the posts have been treated first. If you are building a single-story building, 4 x 4 posts are sufficient. Choose 5 x 5 if you are building a two-story home or your ceilings will be high. Be aware that you will need help to handle them as they are heavy and awkward.

Step Three:

a. Use 16-penny nails or lag screws to attach the rim joists. Make sure your floor joists are a minimum of 2 x 10. These will span 14 feet without needing support beams, but feel free to add supports if you want them.

b. Use standard joist hangers to hang the floor joists on 2-foot centers. You can use offcuts from your 2 x 10 joists as blocks between the floor joists, but make sure they are staggered every 6 to 8 feet. This stops the joists from bouncing or twisting.

Step Four:

a. Use plywood for the subfloor and lay it out. Nail or glue it so it is secure. If you prefer to use planks, ensure the joints are staggered and nail them down.

Step Five:

a. Lay the sills out, marking them on 16-inch centers for the studs. Make sure the wall sections are framed to fit between the posts and frame the windows and doors.

b. Use plywood or sheet siding as exterior wall sheathing and go over the doors and windows. You can cut those out later.

Step Five:

a. Go with a simple roof structure, a single slope similar to a shed roof. Using 16-inch centers, mark out where the rafters will go. However, if you are not using roof insulation, you should go with 2-inch centers. Secure the first and last rafters in place with nails, making sure you have the right-sized overhang.

b. Secure the fascia boards at each end with nails and use them to support the rest of the rafters.

c. If you are using roof shingles, place plywood or boards over the shingles and add black tar paper. Nail on a metal drip edge and place the shingles over the entire roof.

d. You must nail purlins across all the rafters if you choose metal roofing sheets. Then, lay the metal roofing over the top and secure them down.

e. Add soffits beneath the overhang if you need the house winterized or don't want insects getting in.

f. If you want a gable roof, buying ready-made trusses is best, as they are easier to install and cheaper.

Step Six:

a. Install your doors and windows.

b. Add siding if that's what you've opted for, and make sure the entire building is caulked in.

Step Seven:

a. Now is the time to wire your house for electricity, but keep things simple. It's probably best to hire an electrical contractor unless you already know what to do. You can get away with a single circuit for the lights and a single circuit for the kitchen if you don't have large appliances, but splitting the kitchen plugs between two circuits is recommended. That way, you can extend the circuits to other areas.

b. If you want a large range cooker at some point, you will need a 220 circuit only for that and a separate one for a refrigerator. It's best to plan for the future even if you only built a basic house for now.

c. Suppose you are hooking up to the main supply. In that case, the power company will do the connection for you, or if you are going full solar, the installation company can do it.

d. You should also do the plumbing now. Hopefully, you have placed your bathroom and kitchen on the same wall, so the plumbing is all in one place.

Step Eight:

a. Install the wall insulation if you are using it. Use fiberglass batts as they are cheaper and easy to install.

b. If you don't want insulation, you have two choices. Leave the walls open to the framework or install a wall surface. Dry-walling is the easiest and most cost-effective way and can easily be painted over. Alternatively, use pine boarding.

c. You can set up your furniture and furnishings when the walls are up.

Layout Ideas

Layout One:

A small, simple design would be one for one or two people. At 368 sq. feet, it would have a main living area with a 1o-foot kitchen counter, open shelving, and a small sink. The sleeping quarters are a basic platform, big enough for a queen-sized mattress, and built-in drawers beneath.

A small room takes care of a shower/toilet area, while a wood stove provides the heat and cooker. The main wall has double French doors that lead to a large porch, and a small shed at the back works as tool storage.

You can add loft space over the whole area or just part of it, and it has a gable roof and plenty of windows.

Layout Two:

This is a larger space, 672 sq. feet, including a barn and work area. There are two bedrooms, one small, one larger, and high ceilings. The smaller room is enough for a single or bunk bed with storage space beneath, while the larger room has a queen-sized bed platform with storage beneath and sufficient space for small furniture, such as a chest of drawers.

The living area and kitchen are in the center of the layout, with a 10-ft kitchen work surface and an area for a wood fire. The bathroom is a 6 x 7 foot space, while the storage room is 6 x 10 foot. The barn has enough space for a work area, a chicken house, and one stall for a goat, sheep, or cow.

It isn't huge but more than enough for a new homesteader and can easily be extended if needed. Loft space could also be installed.

Layout Three:

This is much larger and consists of a pair of large structures with shed roofs. They are the same size and face each other with a large 20-foot courtyard in between. The courtyard can be left open or covered.

There are 3 bedrooms in one structure: 2 smaller ones with space for single or bunk beds with storage space beneath and a larger one with space for a double bed. The second structure has a large living area and combined kitchen, with a storage area and toilet room.

The courtyard can be fenced in or left open, or it can have trees for shade, whatever you want to do with it.

If you build one of these and choose to build a larger, more permanent structure later, this layout can be converted into a large barn. The building fronts facing the courtyard are high-sided and can easily have trusses between them, supporting a roof. The bedrooms could be turned into animal stalls, while the kitchen/living area could become a work area or somewhere to store food. Built right, the roof above the existing courtyard could be turned into a hayloft, and doors and walls can be used to enclose the space.

All homesteaders want somewhere safe, warm, and dry for themselves and their families, and that is easily accomplished if you keep things simple, at least to start with. And once you are settled, you can either expand your current house or build a new, larger one and repurpose the old one.

Part Two: Living Off the Land I: Plant-Based Food

Chapter 5: Getting Started with Gardening Edibles

Before you move on to this chapter, you should set up your homestead and be ready to start growing your own fruit and vegetables.

Starting a Vegetable Garden

Growing a vegetable garden allows you to be self-sufficient.
https://www.pexels.com/photo/person-checking-his-vegetable-plants-7658823/

If you've never had the space for a vegetable garden before, you should follow a few loose rules to get the best results.

1.   **Choose Somewhere Sunny:** Take a good look around your land. Vegetables need sunlight to grow, so choose somewhere that gets at least 6 to 8 hours of sun daily.

2.   **Make Sure It Is Safe:** It's no good planting vegetables on land that floods when it rains or is prone to strong wind and there are no windbreaks (shrubs, trees, etc.) Make sure the area is safe first.

3.   **Know the First and Last Frosts:** These are important but so often overlooked. Knowing the last frost date in the spring ensures you don't plant heat-loving crops, such as peppers and tomatoes, outside too early. You also need to ensure what you plant can be harvested before the first frost date or is cold-tolerant, like cabbages, leeks, spinach, etc. You also need to be prepared for early and late frosts and have a plan in place to protect your plants.

4.   **Start Small:** So many people get excited when they plant a vegetable garden for the first time that they go overboard and plant a huge garden. Don't do it. Gardens are hard work, so only make your first garden a small one that serves the people you are feeding. Start with a plot about 16 x 10 feet, which will provide enough food for an average family for 4 harvests during the summer, with a little left over to store for winter. You can always expand later.

5.   **Choose Easy Vegetables:** Only grow what you know you will eat and that you can grow easily. Check to see what grows well in your region - the local garden center or other seasoned homesteaders will know. Some of the easiest plants to grow are:
      o   Beans
      o   Beets
      o   Carrots
      o   Cucumbers
      o   Lettuce
      o   Peppers
      o   Radishes
      o   Spinach
      o   Squash

- o Swiss chard
- o Tomatoes
- o Zucchini

6. **Plan Your Garden Space:** The fun part is planning where everything will grow. Draw your garden space on paper and divide it into beds with pathways between them. Plan to grow tall plants at the northern edges, ensuring they don't throw shade over low-growing plants. If you don't have enough space for a big garden, try square-foot gardening. Planned right, it's surprising how much you can grow in a small space.

7. **Prepare the Soil:** There are two basic methods you can use to prepare your soil:

    - o **No-Dig Gardening:** Place cardboard or newspaper over the garden space and top it off with a thick compost layer. Your plants are planted straight into the compost, meaning you don't need to dig or amend your soil.

    - o **Traditional Gardening:** This requires you to till or dig the ground, but make sure it is dry first. If you dig wet soil, it gets compacted, and your plants will struggle to grow. Till the garden, then rake it over and till it again. Once the soil is loosened off, add well-rotted manure or compost and till it again. This should be done in the fall. You can hand dig it if you don't have access to a tiller, but this is a lot of work. Dig it over, add manure or compost, and rake it smooth.

8. **Start Planting:** If planting seeds directly into the ground, follow the package instructions for spacing. Cover them with soil, firm them down, and water. You want to keep the soil moist but not overly wet until the plants have started growing and are established. If you start with seedlings, harden them off before planting. This means placing them outdoors during the day and bringing them in overnight, gradually increasing how long you leave them outdoors.

9. **Add Mulch:** This ensures the soil retains moisture, stops dirt splashing onto your plants when it rains, and keeps the weeds down, all saving you a lot of work.

10. **Watering:** Watering is the most crucial part of growing veggies, and your garden will need around an inch of water per week. If

you get plenty of rain, you don't need to worry, but you will definitely need to get the hose out in dry areas. Soaker hoses are the most efficient way of watering as the water goes right to the roots and nowhere else.

As you can see, starting a vegetable garden isn't too hard, but don't underestimate the work involved. A well-planned, properly located garden can feed you and your family all year if you do it right.

Chapter 6: Harvesting and Making Your Own Plant-Based Food

The more you work in your garden, the more you will learn. This is very true, especially when growing fruit and vegetables. Most seed packets give full planting instructions and also give you an idea of how long the plant takes to mature. However, those are only guidelines because many factors can influence harvest time.

Knowing the "official" number of days a plant takes to mature is a good starting place, but you also need to use common sense to know when your vegetables are ready to pick. The first part of this chapter will guide you through harvesting, while the second part provides a few recipes to help you get started using your harvest.

Harvesting Principles

There are principals you should follow when it comes to harvesting.
https://unsplash.com/photos/yellow-and-red-tomatoes-on-green-plastic-crate-hmoDcZnB7uw

These principles give you an idea of how and when you should harvest:

- **Peak Flavor and Nutrition:** Some vegetables don't need to be entirely ripe to be at their best. Summer squash, turnips, beans, and peas should be harvested when they're tender and young. On the other hand, those that should be ripe for full flavor include melons, winter squash, peppers, and tomatoes.
- **Size:** This is a good indicator, but knowing when vegetables are ready to pick takes practice. Check the seed packets for a good indication because all varieties differ.
- **Pick Often:** Many gardeners make the mistake of not harvesting regularly. If you leave your beans on the plant, they can quickly turn tough, while a ripe but small zucchini can quickly expand and become overripe in just a couple of days. Plants have one goal, which is to reproduce. By picking often, you keep that plant producing plenty of food for you. Stop picking, and the plant stops producing.
- **Use the Correct Tools:** A number of vegetables can be finger-picked, including peas, lettuce, and kale, but you'll find many

more that need to be cut using scissors or cutters. Finally, forks are best when it comes to root crops.

- **The Ideal Conditions:** Vegetables are at their best when they are harvested, but that quality quickly declines. When the dew has dried and the crops are at their juiciest and sweetest, early morning is the ideal time to harvest. Harvesting during the hottest part of the day is not recommended, as leafy crops such as kale and lettuce can wilt quickly.

- **Harvest with Care:** Cucumbers and tomatoes are examples of vining plants that require appropriate trellising to prevent breakage of the plant stems. Avoid tearing the veggies off the plant, as this might harm it and make it more susceptible to disease. Additionally, you should avoid working in your vegetable patch during rainy seasons since you may inadvertently transfer fungi and diseases from one plant to another.

- **Outer Leaves First:** Some crops grow from the middle outwards – think cabbage, lettuce, and similar leafy veggies. Unless you are picking the whole plant, start with the outer leaves, leaving the center to continue growing.

Harvesting Guidelines

This is not a complete list, but some of the more common vegetables you are likely to grow:

Arugula:
- Pinch or cut leaves when 2 to 3 inches. Young leaves taste best, but you can eat older leaves until the plant bolts.

Asparagus:
- Harvest when 6 to 8 inches tall with tightly closed tips.
- Break them by bending or cutting them off below or at soil level. Do not cut any nearby spears that haven't come through yet.
- Continue harvesting for 4 to 8 weeks and stop once the spears are thinner with open tips.
- Be aware that an asparagus bed can take at least 3 years to develop before you can harvest it.

Beans - Snap:

- Bush and pole beans are harvested when they are about pencil-thick, with small beans inside.

- Do not harvest immature, thin pods, as they won't have much flavor.

- Avoid harvesting heavy, protruding pods since the beans within are bland and rough. Harvest them as dry beans by leaving them on the plant.

Beans - Dry:

- When the pods turn yellow and dry out in the fall, mature pole or bush beans are harvested.

- Snip them from the vine and spread them in a warm, dry place to dry for 2 to 4 weeks.

- When 100% dry, shell the beans - they should be hard and shiny - and store them.

Beets:

- Harvest beets at about 1 ½ to 2 ½ inches in diameter (Any larger, and they may be woody with less flavor)

- Beets must be harvested before the ground freezes

Broccoli:

- Harvest when the head is 3 to 6 inches in diameter, with dark green, closed buds.

- Cut it about 6 inches below the head, and smaller heads will grow off the side.

Brussels Sprouts: Harvest from the bottom when the sprouts are 1 to 1 ½ inches in diameter, twisting or cutting them off.

Cabbage: Harvest when the cabbage head is about football-sized or bigger and solid. Any longer, and the cabbages will split, expanding in size.

Carrots:

- Most varieties can be harvested at about an inch round. Pull one up to check the size.

- Spring-planted carrots should be harvested as soon as they mature, or they will become bitter.

- Fall-planted carrots can stay in beds over the winter so long as they are covered by straw or grown in a polytunnel.

Cauliflower:

- Keep an eye on the maturity date indicated on the seed packet, as cauliflower can rapidly transition from its peak to beyond it.
- The head should be regular-shaped with tight curds and not yellow. Left too long, the plants will bolt.
- Cut just below the head, leaving some leaves on.

Collards:

- Harvest leaves when they are 6 to 8 inches long and tender, as older leaves are tough.
- Start with the large leaves at the bottom and leave smaller leaves to keep growing.

Corn:

- You can test the corn for ripeness when the silks turn brown and dry. Feel the tip through the husk. It is ready to pick if rounded but not if it tapers and is thinner at the top.
- Alternatively, use a fingernail to prick a kernel. If the liquid is milky, the corn is ready.
- Harvest first thing in the morning, as the corn is sweeter.

Cucumbers:

- Pickling cucumbers should be cut when 2 to 6 inches long.
- Slicing cucumbers should be cut when 6 to 8 inches long.
- In all cases, they should have dark green, glossy skin. If yellow or dull, the cucumbers will be bitter and tasteless.

Eggplants:

- Eggplants must be cut with a little stem left on.
- Wait until they are about half the recommended mature size and have a glossy, all-over color.
- They are overripe if they are dull and soft.

Garlic:

- You can harvest your garlic when the tops start to dry off.
- Make sure you aren't bruising the bulb as you are lifting the plant out.

- Clean the soil off with water and leave them to dry. Make sure they're placed on a net tray and in a dry shade that is warm for approximately two to three weeks. Make sure it has good air circulation.
- When they are dry, cut off the tops and store them.

Kale:
- Leaves can be harvested as needed when 6 to 8 inches long.
- Start with the outer leaves and cut them off at the base.
- Baby leaves can be harvested for salads when they are 2 to 3 inches long.

Leeks:
- Harvest when the leek is an inch thick.
- Pull the entire plant from the soil.

Lettuce:
- Lettuce heads can be harvested when they are medium-firm, feel full, and are approximately 6 inches round.
- Leaf lettuces can be harvested when the leaves are 3 to 4 inches tall.
- They will produce new leaves, so continue harvesting regularly until the plant produces a stem in the center. This indicates the lettuce is about to bolt.

Melons:
- Cantaloupes should be harvested when the fruit separates easily from the stem, they have a sweet smell, and the rind is yellow. Harvest as soon as the dew has dried in the morning.
- Honeydews should be harvested when the rind is yellow or white all over. They will need to be cut from the stem and should be harvested once the dew has dried.
- Watermelons are ready when the underside turns cream or yellow, and the topside is a dull color. They must be cut off the plant, leaving a couple of inches of stem attached.

Onions:
- Green onions (scallions) are ready to harvest when the tops are 6 inches tall and can be pulled out whole.

- Bulb onions are harvested when the bulbs are about 1 to 2 inches round, and the tops are brown and have fallen over. Pull the whole plant, and dry the onions by spreading them out or hanging them somewhere warm, dry, and ventilated for a couple of weeks. Then, brush the soil off, cut off the tops, and trim the roots before storing.

Parsnips:

- Allow a few light frosts before you harvest parsnips as it improves the taste, or leave them in-ground, covered in straw, for the winter, harvesting as needed.
- Ensure you harvest before the spring, as they lose their flavor if you allow new growth to shoot from them.
- Pull the entire plant, trim the foliage to about ¼-inch, and store in a root cellar or refrigerator.

Peas:

- Snow peas can be harvested when the pods are a mature length but before the peas have filled out the pod.
- Sugar snap peas can be harvested when the pods and peas are plump.
- Shelling peas are harvested when the pods are plump, green, and firm and the peas have grown.

Peppers:

- Sweet peppers can be harvested unripe or ripe. Cut them off so you don't damage the plant. You can leave the peppers to ripen – yellow, orange, and red – to get the full sweetness, but you can also harvest them green. If you do, harvest regularly so the plant produces more. You can always leave later peppers to ripen fully, giving you the best of both worlds.
- Hot peppers can again be harvested ripe or unripe by cutting them off. Red peppers are hotter than green. Make sure you wear gloves, as they can burn your skin.

Potatoes:

- When you harvest potatoes depends on their variety.
- New potatoes can be harvested 6 to 8 weeks after planting, just after flowering. You can harvest a few potatoes from the plant by digging gently into the soil and leaving the rest to mature.

- Main crop potatoes are harvested about 2 weeks after the tops have died. Dig them out carefully so you don't bruise or damage any. If you do, they must be eaten quickly because they cannot be stored.
- Leave the potatoes on top of the soil to cure for a couple of weeks (unless the weather is wet), and store good potatoes somewhere dark, cool, and frost-free.

Pumpkins:
- The pumpkin should be a uniform, deep color, and the stem should start to dry before harvesting.
- Cut them off the vines, leaving a small amount of stem attached, and spread them out to dry for 10 days. They must be somewhere warm, dry, and ventilated.
- They can be stored in a dry, cool, ventilated area.

Radishes:
- Spring radishes are harvested when small and mild. They get woody and bitter if you leave them in the ground too long.

Shallots:
- Shallots are mature when the bulbs are 1 to 1 ½ inches round, and the tops are brown.
- Cut off the tops, let the shallots dry for a week in a warm place, and then store them.

Spinach:
- Harvest spinach leaves when they are 3 inches long, starting with the outer leaves.
- Continue to harvest as needed until a center stem appears, indicating the plant is starting to bolt.

Squash:
- Summer squash should be harvested when small for good flavor. Harvest after the dew has dried and cut them from the vine. Check your plants and harvest daily, as they can quickly go past their best.
- Winter squash is ready when the fruit is colored all over and the vines are dying off. Cut from the plant, leaving a bit of stem attached, and cure them somewhere warm for 10 days before storing.

Sweet Potatoes:

- These are ready to harvest when the foliage has turned yellow.
- Harvest before the first frost unless grown in a polytunnel.
- Lift the tuners gently from the ground, taking care not to bruise or damage them.
- Cure for one day in the sun, then in the shade for another week or so.

Tomatoes:

- Harvest when they are ripe but firm.
- Harvest before the first frost. Check daily and harvest ripened fruit, as this will encourage more growth.

Turnips:

- Harvest when they are about 2 to 3 inches in diameter for a sweet taste.
- Harvest before the first frosts.

Plant-Based Recipes

When you harvest your fruit and vegetables, you should use them quickly, store them for winter, or turn them into something else. The remainder of this chapter provides some recipes to help you use some of your harvest.

Strawberry Jam

You can also use blackberries, blueberries, or raspberries in this recipe. The lemon peel provides natural pectin to help thicken up the jam. You can use any sugar – granulated, coconut, maple, or agave syrup, whatever takes your fancy, but try to keep all your ingredients organic.

You can add chia seeds and agar agar if you want an even thicker jam.

Ingredients:

- 2.2 lb. strawberries (or other fruit of your choice).
- 8.8 oz. sugar
- 1 whole lemon
- 1 tsp. chia seeds – OPTIONAL
- 6 tsp. agar – OPTIONAL

Instructions:

1. Rinse and hull the strawberries and chop each one into four parts. Put them in a bowl, add thin lemon peel strips, and squeeze the lemon juice over the top.

2. Sprinkle with the sugar and mix until it dissolves. Marinate for at least an hour, preferably overnight.

3. Add to a pan, remove the peel, and bring to a boil. Simmer for 15 minutes, stirring frequently.

4. Using an immersion blender, blend the mixture for a couple of seconds - skip if you prefer chunky jam.

5. OPTIONAL - add the chia and agar to make a thicker jam, which is recommended if you want to use the jam in cakes or pies. Then, boil it for 5 minutes so the agar is activated.

6. Transfer to jars and leave to cool before storing in a refrigerator. Use within 7 days.

Roasted Cherry Tomato Sauce

Ingredients:

- 6 cups cherry tomatoes.
- 1 onion
- 3 cloves garlic OR 3 tbsp. minced garlic.
- 3 tbsp. olive oil
- ½ tsp. salt
- ½ tsp. pepper

Instructions:

1. Preheat your oven to 400°F and place greaseproof paper on a baking sheet.

2. Chop the onion into quarters and lay it on the baking sheet in a single layer with the tomatoes and garlic.

3. Drizzle oil over, season with salt and pepper, and stir to coat the veggies in oil.

4. Bake until the tomatoes begin bursting and brown off a little on top, about 45 to 50 minutes.

5. Place everything in a blender and blitz to a creamy sauce, about 2 to 3 minutes.

6. Cool and store in the refrigerator until needed.

Canned Zucchini Spread

Ingredients:

- 5 loosely packed cups of chopped onions
- 8 1/3 cups chopped carrots
- 6 2/3 cup chopped zucchini
- 2 chopped celery stalks
- 2 ½ cups chopped bell peppers
- 2 chopped jalapenos
- 5 loosely packed cups of chopped tomatoes
- 2 large cloves of garlic
- 1 to 3 tbsp. salt
- 1 tsp. black pepper
- 1 cup apple cider or white vinegar
- Fresh chopped parsley, dill, and cilantro to taste
- Oil for frying

Instructions:

1. Use water or oil to sauté the onions, then add the carrots and stir. Crush the garlic, add that to the pan, and then add the celery and zucchini.

2. Stir, cooking until the veggies have softened, then add the tomatoes, peppers, and vinegar. Simmer for 10 minutes if you are using a pressure canner or up to an hour if not.

3. Add the spices and herbs, cook for a few more minutes, then process in the pressure canner at 11 pounds pressure for 20 minutes for pint jars and 25 minutes for quarts. Don't forget to adjust the pressure for altitude if needed.

Sprouted Bread

Ingredients:

- 1 cup warm wate
- 1 ½ tsp. dry yeast
- 2 tbsp. organic honey
- 2 ¼ cups sprouted wheat flour.
- ¼ cup oat bran *
- 1 tbsp. extra-virgin olive oil

• 1 tsp. salt

* If oat bran isn't available, you can put ¼ cup of quick oats in a blender or processor and process it into fine-milled flour.

Instructions:

1. Add the honey to water, stir to dissolve it, and then add the yeast. Leave it until it bubbles.

2. Put the oat bran, wheat flour, and salt in a bowl and whisk gently to combine. Add the foamy yeast to the dry mixture, add the oil, and stir to combine thoroughly. Leave it for 10 minutes.

3. Lightly flour a surface and tip the dough onto it. Knead it for five minutes, then place it in an oiled bowl and cover it with a clean cloth. Leave it for an hour somewhere warm until it doubles in size.

4. Oil a standard loaf pan, form the dough gently into a log, and place it into the pan. Leave until it has risen to the top edge of the pan, about an hour again.

5. About 10 minutes before the time is up, preheat your oven to 350°F.

6. Bake the loaf for about 30 to 35 minutes. It should sound hollow when you tap it and be golden brown. If it browns too quickly, cover it with a foil tent.

7. Once cooked, leave it to cool for about 5 minutes, then transfer it onto a cooling rack. Cool completely before slicing.

Baby Puree

Making organic baby puree with your harvest is pretty simple. All you need are the veggies and a blender. The following recipe uses 6 sweet potatoes, but you can use any of the following with the same recipe:

• Beets
• Butternut squash
• Carrots
• Green beans
• Greens
• Parsnips
• Peas

• Turnips

Instructions:

1. Peel your chosen vegetables and chop them into chunks.

2. If you have an electric or stovetop steamer, place them in the basket. Add about an inch of water to the pan (do not add the basket yet) and bring it to a simmer.

3. Add the veggie basket and cook, covered until soft. Alternatively, cook them in a microwave.

4. Place the cooked vegetables in a blender and pulse to a smooth consistency. If necessary, add a little of the water you used for steaming.

5. Allow it to cool and refrigerate until needed, or divide it into portions and freeze.

You can also use fruit, such as:

• Apples

• Blackberries

• Blueberries

• Mango

• Peaches

• Pears

• Pineapple

• Strawberries

Spicy Plum and Apple Chutney

Ingredients:

• ½ garlic bulb

• Thumb-sized chunk of fresh ginger

• 1 large onion

• 1 lb. 2 oz. apples

• ½ tsp. cumin seed

• 1 stick cinnamon

• 1 cup apple cider vinegar

• 1/2 of 1 bulb of garlic

• A small thumb-size piece of ginger

• 1 large onion

- 1 pound and 2 ounces of apples
- 1 lb. 2 oz. plums
- 1/2 teaspoon cumin seeds
- 1 cinnamon stick
- 1 cup apple cider vinegar
- 1 cup golden caster sugar
- ½ tsp. salt

Instructions:

1. Sterilize your mason jars for 30 minutes at 300°F.
2. Peel and sliver the garlic, shred the ginger finely and chop the onion into small pieces.
3. Put them in a pan with the vinegar, salt, and spices. Peel and chop the apples, add them to the pan, and bring them to the boil. Reduce the heat, cover, and simmer it for half an hour.
4. Remove the plum stones, chop them, and add them to the pan. Stir in the sugar and cook for about 40 minutes, occasionally stirring.
5. Spoon the mixture into the jars, cover with a fabric or plastic top, and tie it on.
6. Store for a month before you use it to let the flavors develop.

Spiced Apple Chutney

Ingredients:

- 1 ½ cups white sugar
- 1 ½ cups white vinegar
- 4 tart green apples
- ¼ cup golden raisins
- ¼ cup dried apricots, diced
- ¼ cup shallots, diced
- 5 thick fresh ginger slices
- ¼ tsp. Aleppo or red pepper flakes
- 1 star anise
- 2 minced garlic cloves
- 1 tsp. kosher salt
- ½ tsp. yellow mustard seed

Instructions:

1. Put the sugar and vinegar in a large pan and whisk. Peel, core, and chop the apples into small, even chunks. Add them to the pan with the ginger, raisins, apricots, shallots, star anise, and pepper flakes. Stir and heat to a simmer.

2. Reduce the heat to medium-low, add the salt, mustard seeds, and garlic, and simmer for 40 to 45 minutes. The apples should be soft, and the liquid should be reduced.

3. Remove the pan from the heat and let it cool before lifting the star anise and ginger out.

4. Place the chutney in the refrigerator until chilled and season with pepper flakes and salt.

Chapter 7: Canning and Preserving Plant-Based Food

It sometimes seems like all or nothing when you grow your own fruit and vegetables. Sometimes, you get little for your effort, and at other times, you'll have so much you won't know what to do with it. That's where safe food preservation comes in, allowing you to grow enough throughout the growing season to feed yourself all year.

Canning

Canning is a popular method of preservation.
https://unsplash.com/photos/a-wooden-shelf-filled-with-lots-of-jars-of-food-bhni1zsPiio

One of the most popular methods of preservation is canning, and there are two main types:

- Water bath
- Pressure

Which one you use is determined by the food's acidity levels – low-acid foods must be water bath canned, while high-acid foods must be pressure canned.

Food Acidity

Low-Acid

These include most vegetables (not pickled foods or acidified tomatoes) and meat. They do not have sufficient acid to stop bacteria that would be killed by boiling water. The worst bacterium is Clostridium botulinum, which is responsible for a deadly food poisoning called botulism. Using a pressure canner destroys the botulinum spores because it uses much higher temperatures.

High-Acid

These include most fruits, although tomatoes are on the low-high acid borderline and must be processed using vinegar, citric acid, or lemon juice to increase their acidity levels. It also includes pickled and fermented foods, jellies, and jams (unless made with low-acid vegetables.)

Let's look at the two popular canning types.

Boiling Water Bath Canner

The food is heated when the jar is submerged in boiling water. A temperature of 212°F must be maintained to kill bacteria and enzymes, and each recipe will specify the exact processing time. These are usually given for altitudes of 1,000 feet or lower above sea level. Remember that water requires a lower temperature to boil at high altitudes, so processing time is usually longer.

Pressure Canner

Heat is applied when the canner is sealed, forcing pressure to build up inside. This creates steam, which pushes air out, and when the canner vents are shut, the canner only contains pressurized steam. This is much hotter than boiling water, but again, adjustments for altitude are required.

Canning Procedures

No matter which type of canner you use, there are set procedures you must follow.

- **Choose Your Jars and Lids:** although commercial single-use jars may also be used, Mason jars are ideal. However, you may have trouble getting lids to fit these. You can get jars in many sizes, but most recipes use quart and pint jars. You can use larger half-gallon jars for juices, and most jars can be reused if cleaned and sterilized. Lids should be flat metal disks with a separate screw band and edged by a sealing compound. Never reuse lids. Bands can be used again if they are not rusty or damaged.

- **Hot or Raw Pack?** Raw packing requires the food to be packed raw into the jars. However, as it can float inside the jar, it may discolor within a couple of months. Hot packing requires the food to be boiled, simmered, and filled into the jars hot. This ensures the air is removed from the food, shrinking it and stopping it from floating. It also allows more food to go into the jars.

General Guidelines

- Always use well-tested recipes, i.e., those from the USDA.
- Mason jars can withstand higher temperatures than single-use jars, especially for pressure canning.
- Jars should never be filled cold. Always heat them in simmering water or a dishwasher.
- Always leave the right headspace. Jams, juices, and jellies require ¼-inch, pickles, tomatoes, and fruits require ½-inch, and veggies and meats require an inch. Too little means food may be forced into the seal, stopping it from working, and too much can weaken the seal with a low vacuum.
- Use a bubble remover or another plastic tool to remove air bubbles.
- Clean the jar rims before putting the lids and bands on.
- Two-piece lids should be used – a screw band and a flat disk.
- Lids should only be finger-tight.
- Use a jar lifter to get the jars into and out of the canner.
- Do not tilt jars when you move them.

- Use the correct processing method per the recipe.
- Adjust pressure and time for altitude.
- All jars should be set a couple of inches apart on a thick towel or heat-proof board to cool.
- Never turn the jars upside down or retighten the screw bands.

Water Bath Canning Procedure:

1. Follow the guidelines.
2. Half-fill the canner with water and preheat it: 140°F for raw-packing and 180°F for hot-packing
3. Put the jars on the rack inside the canner.
4. Pour in more water if needed to ensure the jars are submerged by at least an inch.
5. Put the lid on and leave it on during the process.
6. Turn the heat right up until the water is boiling. Reduce the heat to a gentle boil.
7. If the water stops boiling, turn the heat back up and start over.
8. Once the time is up, turn off the heat, remove the lid, and leave the jars for 5 minutes. Then, lift them out and place them somewhere to cool.

Pressure Canning Procedure:

1. Follow the guidelines.
2. Put 2 to 3 inches of water in the canner and put the jars on a rack at the bottom.
3. Tighten the lid and heat the water to boiling, venting the steam for 10 minutes. Then you can close the petcock or add weights.
4. Add the pressure or weight regulator.
5. The pressure must then rise and be maintained for the time stated in the recipe. If the pressure drops, you must start over.
6. Once processing is finished, turn off the heat and let the pressure cool until the pressure is at zero. Wait for 2 minutes, and then remove the regulator. Wait a further 10 minutes, and then remove the lid and set the jars aside to cool.

Testing the Seal

Jars must cool for 12 to 24 hours, and then you should press on the lid center. If it moves, the jar is not sealed. If it doesn't, and you cannot remove the lid once the band is removed, the jar is properly sealed.

Storage

- Take the screw bands off and wash the jars.
- Store somewhere dark, cool, and dry at a temperature of 50 to 70°F.

Dehydration

Dehydrated foods are becoming more popular.
https://unsplash.com/photos/flatlay-photography-of-citrus-and-dragon-atzWFItRHy8

Dehydrated foods are becoming very popular and are not just good for snacks. You can serve them with dips, add them to stews and soups, or even use them as pizza toppers. It's a simple way to preserve certain foods and make your own fruit leather, vegetable or fruit chips, and jerky.

1. **Pick Your Produce at Its Peak:** Contrary to popular belief, you cannot use old, bruised, or damaged food. Drying food concentrates the flavor, so always start with food at its prime.

2. **Clean and Peel:** Wash fruit and vegetables thoroughly and peel them. You don't have to do this, but peel does become tough during dehydration.

3. **Slice Thinly:** Use a sharp knife or mandolin to slice the food into uniform pieces, ¼ to 1/8-inch thick. That way, they all dehydrate at the same rate.

4. **Dip It in Citrus Water:** This is really only for fruit that goes brown, such as apples and bananas. Dip it in a solution of 50%

water and 50% lemon juice for about 10 minutes. Then remove and pat dry.

5. **Blanch It:** This is for starchy foods like potatoes and peas. Boil for a few minutes, and immediately put them in an ice bath to stop the cooking process.

Using a Dehydrator:

These are simple to use. Simply layer the food on the trays, set the dial, and turn it on. Fruit should typically be dehydrated at 135°F, while vegetables require 125°F. Times will vary according to the food being dehydrated, its initial ripeness, slice size, and the day's humidity.

Using an Oven:

While this is an option, be aware that ovens may be hotter and don't always heat consistently. The oven must be preheated to its lowest temperature, and cooling racks must be placed on lined baking trays. Layer the food on the trays and cook. You must monitor them carefully as drying time is shorter than a dehydrator. You will also need to rotate the baking pans for even drying.

Storing Dried Produce:

Cool the food completely and store it in airtight containers, like Mason jars, snap-top lids, or Ziploc bags. They should be stored in a dark, cool place. Shake a container after a few days, and if you see any moisture, place the food back in the dehydrator or over for a while. Once dried properly, food can last for several months.

Pickling and Fermenting

Fermenting and pickling are age-old preservation methods commonly but incorrectly discussed interchangeably. While there is some overlap between them, they are two separate methods.

Pickling:

Pickling is defined as preserving food in acidic brine and has been used for thousands of years as a preservation method. It doesn't take much to do, either, making food taste sour, with a softer texture.

You can quick-pickle foods easily by boiling a solution of water, vinegar, sugar, and salt and pouring it over the prepared vegetables. You can also add a pickling spice mix. This method destroys microorganisms and bacteria.

Fermenting:

This is also a simple method and is older than pickling. It uses yeast, bacteria, or other microorganisms to turn food carbs into alcohol. There are two fermentation types:

- **Alcoholic:** commonly used in beer, wine, and bread. Yeast and bacteria break pyruvate down into carbon dioxide and ethanol.
- **Lactic Acid:** the pyruvate molecules break down even further into lactic acid.

Fermented foods are rich in probiotics, making them an excellent choice for the digestive system. Kimchi, miso paste, and sauerkraut are popular fermented foods.

The Pickling Liquid:

- **Vinegar:** use white or white wine vinegar for a clear color, but red wine, rice, apple cider, or a combination of vinegar also works well.
- **Water:** needed to dilute the vinegar.
- **Salt:** a preservation agent that adds flavor.
- **Sugar:** helps balance the acidic taste of vinegar.
- **Whole Spices:** use coriander seeds, mustard seeds, dill seeds, fennel seeds, celery seeds, cumin seeds, star anise, allspice, clove, and/or black peppercorns.
- **Fresh herbs:** dill works best, but basil and cilantro also work.
- **Garlic cloves:** you can also use onion slices.

How to Pickle Veggies:

1. **Wash Your Vegetables.** Peel them if needed and slice those that need slicing.
2. **Pack the Vegetables into the Jars.** Layer them with herbs, whole spices, and raw onion, ginger, or garlic.
3. **Heat the Pickling Liquid.** Do this while filling your jars, allowing the liquid to boil.
4. **Fill the Jars.** Pour the liquid over the vegetables, leaving ½-inch headspace, wipe the jars, and put the lids on.
5. **Cool Them.** Leave the jars on the counter to cool for a few hours, then refrigerate for 12 to 24 hours. This will allow the flavors to develop. If you can leave them for a few days, it's even better!

Sauerkraut
Ingredients:
- 4.4 lb. firm white or pale green cabbage, outer leaves removed
- 6 tbsp. flaky sea salt OR 3 tbsp. coarse crystal sea salt
- 1 tsp. whole peppercorns
- 1 tsp. caraway seeds

Instructions:
1. Sterilize a large bowl with boiling water, then wash your hands thoroughly.
2. Thinly shred the cabbage and layer it in the bowl with the salt. Massage the cabbage gently for five minutes to get the salt into it, then stop for five minutes before massaging again. The cabbage should end up reduced and coated in brine.
3. Stir in the peppercorns and caraway seeds and cover the cabbage surface with plastic wrap, pressing the air bubbles out. You should see the brine level rise to cover the cabbage.
4. Cover the entire bowl with a clean towel and leave it somewhere dark and cool for 5 days or more. The longer you can leave it, the better the flavor, so try to leave it for 2 to 6 weeks or until the bubbles have stopped.
5. Check it daily to allow gases to be released and stir it to get rid of the bubbles. Remove any scum that forms.
6. Make sure you keep the temperature consistently cool, 64 to 68°F. Any cooler and fermentation will take longer – and any warmer, it may turn moldy.
7. When the cabbage is how you want it, pack it into small sterilized jars and store it in the refrigerator for up to six months.

Dill Pickles
Ingredients:
- 8 to 10 pickling cucumbers
- 4 cloves of garlic, halved.
- 2 tsp. mustard seeds
- 2 tsp. peppercorns
- 2 cups water
- 2 cups distilled white vinegar (5%)

- ¼ cup cane sugar
- 2 tbsp. sea salt
- Fresh dill sprigs

Instructions:

1. Slice the pickles into 4 pieces lengthwise to make spears, or slice them thinly widthwise to make pickle chips.
2. Divide them between 4 8-oz. or 2 16-oz. sterilized jars.
3. Divide the mustard seeds, garlic, and peppercorns between the jars and add dill to each one.
4. Combine the sugar, salt, water, and vinegar in a pan and heat over medium heat. Stir to dissolve the salt and sugar, and then leave it to cool a little.
5. Pour the liquid into the jars, put the lids on, and leave to cool for a few hours.
6. Refrigerate for 5 to 6 days for spears or a couple of days for chips.
7. These can be stored in the refrigerator for several weeks.

Root Cellaring

In the days of old, people didn't have refrigerators to store their food. Indeed, many didn't have the luxury of electricity, so they used root cellars to store their food, especially root vegetables. Root cellars use the earth's natural insulation and cooling properties to stop food from going off in the summer and freezing in winter.

Root cellars aren't just for root vegetables, though. You can also store your canned foods, pickles, fruit, other vegetables, dairy and meats, homemade juices, and alcoholic drinks.

The beauty of a root cellar is that if the electricity goes out, you don't have to worry about food spoiling. You can harvest from your garden all summer long and store it away for winter, saving you a ton of money in electric and shopping costs.

Basic Requirements

You need to consider a few things if you are thinking about having a root cellar on your homestead:

- **Legal Requirements:** You must consult your local building department to see the requirements for building a root cellar.

Some areas will require you to have a building permit.

- **Temperature:** Your climate is important because root cellars use the earth for cooling and insulation. If you live in southern states where the climate is typically hotter, root cellars don't work so well. The temperature in the cellar must be kept at between 32 to 40°F.

- **Location:** Be careful about where you build your cellar. For example, don't plan to build near the sewage or septic system, where the water table is high, or in areas where flooding is a problem. Also, consider the size of the cellar. On average, they are typically 8 x 8 feet.

- **Humidity:** Root cellars need 85 to 95% humidity, no lower. If your cellar floor is gravel or dirt, this won't be a problem because the earth will do it for you.

- **Ventilation:** Root cellars need air circulation, so your cellar must be airtight with the right ventilation system.

- **Darkness:** Your root cellar needs to be dark, or your veggies may start sprouting, change color, lose their nutrients, or even go off. If your cellar has windows, they must be covered in blackout material, and the lights should only be turned on when absolutely needed.

Different Types of Root Cellar

There are several types of root cellar, some attached to your home, others not:

Basement

If you have a basement, you're in luck. Part of it could be turned into a root cellar, but there are a couple of recommendations to follow:

- The northeast corner foundation walls should be used as two sides of the cellar.
- The other two walls should be built using boards and studs
- The ceiling, interior walls, ducts, pipes, and door must be insulated to ensure the room stays cool

Hole in the Ground

This is your traditional cellar and is simple enough to build. Dig a large hole in the ground or, if you live on hilly land, into the sides of a hill. Reinforce the sides so you have a room and put a doorway in.

Obviously, it's a bit more complex than that, but you get the idea.

Barrel

If space is limited, you could have a simple barrel cellar. This just requires burying a large garbage can or barrel into a hole in the ground. The food should be stored inside the can with straw, earth heaped around the outside, and the lid covered with mulch or straw and a plastic sheet. This will keep root vegetables fresh no matter how cold it gets.

Storing Your Vegetables

Always suit your produce before you store it. You should only store mature, firm vegetables and fruit that are undamaged and unblemished. Damaged, rotten, or overripe food can contaminate everything else, so these should be composted or used immediately.

Use baskets, mesh bags, or other containers with good air circulation, and make sure there are no sharp edges. Some foods should not be stored together or even near each other. The following summary will give you an idea of winter veggie storage requirements:

- **Cabbages:** best kept in the ground, covered in heavy mulch. Alternatively, hang them from their roots in an external building. It must not be stored indoors as it gives off ethylene gas. Store at 32 to 40°F, 80 to 90% humidity.

- **Garlic and Onions:** cure or dry them somewhere ventilated for 2 to 3 weeks. Then, hang them in the cellar as they are or in mesh bags. Keep the cellar at 40 to 50°F, 60 to 70% humidity.

- **Potatoes:** should be cured for a few weeks first. Layer firm, undamaged, or unblemished potatoes in one layer somewhere dark. Cover them with newspaper and leave them for 2 weeks at 45 to 60°F, then store them in total darkness in wooden boxes (covered), paper bags, dry sand, or tin buckets. If they begin sprouting, they are too warm. Do not store near apples or onions, as these hasten sprouting.

- **Squash and Pumpkins:** Leave the stems on when you harvest, as this lessens the risk of disease. Store them in a cool, dry place, 40 to 60°F, 60 to 70% humidity, in mesh bags or placed on shelves, not touching each other.

- **Root Crops:** can stay in the ground covered in mulch and withstand temperatures of 28°F or above. To store in a cellar, leave an inch of stem and top and layer in boxes or baskets. Put sand or sphagnum moss between each layer and store at 32 to 40°F, 80 to 90% humidity.

- **Citrus:** store at 40 to 50°F, 60 to 70% humidity in mesh bags or baskets. Oranges can go as low as 32 to 34°F.

- **Pome Fruits:** this includes pears and apples, and they need to be stored in very cold temperatures, as near to 32°F as possible, at 80 to 90% humidity. Store in boxes layered with moss or sand, in plastic bags with holes, or individually wrapped in paper and layered in boxes. As they emit ethylene gas, they cannot be stored near any other crop.

Part Three: Living Off the Land II: Animals, Meat, and Dairy

Chapter 8: The Buzz on Beekeeping

The world is abuzz with talk of the bees dying off, but why is this such a hot issue? The answer is simple – bees are one of the most important pollinators for food crops. However, because so many chemicals are used on commercially grown food, and partly due to climate change, the bees are dying. If people don't repopulate them quickly, food crops will disappear, too.

Grocery stores would stock fewer vegetables and fruit. You wouldn't be able to buy anything with honey, coffee, chocolate, almonds, etc. There would be little beef and milk because the plants used to feed the cattle would not be pollinated. They even help trees and plants grow, providing the planet with oxygen. It's safe to say that, without bees, we would struggle to survive. And, if no plants were pollinated, they wouldn't reproduce, and other wildlife would lose a food supply and shelter.

How to Keep Bees

To keep bees, you need certain equipment.
https://unsplash.com/photos/person-in-white-pants-and-white-shoes-standing-on-brown-wooden-table-LZ3Ffa_Yl7E

Keeping bees is not something you can just decide to do. You need specific equipment before getting the bees, and it's tough for a beginner to know where to start.

The essential equipment you need:

- **Hives:** obviously, you need a hive, and there are two primary ones to choose from. Langstroth hives are the most common wooden sections stacked on top of one another and containing hanging frames. Top bar hives contain frames hanging from the top bar, with honeycomb hanging from the frames.

- **Bee Suit:** these are designed to cover you completely to protect you from bee stings. A complete suit is made from heavy fabric and includes a hat, veil, gloves, and boots.

- **Hive Tool:** this is a small tool but one of the most important, as it can help you separate the boxes, get the frames out safely, and get the excess propolis and wax from the rest of the hive.

- **Smoker:** an essential piece, a smoker keeps the bees calm as the smoke covers their pheromones. This lessens the risk of being stung by upset bees.

- **Bee Brush:** this helps you get the bees off the frames when needed, get them into boxes when they swarm, or even get them off you.
- **Queen Catcher:** if you need to keep the queen separate for a while, this tool helps you do it without hurting her.
- **Feeder:** bees are good at feeding themselves through the spring and summer months, but they need food throughout fall and winter, too. A feeder allows you to feed them on dry sugar, honey, or sugar syrup.
- **Capping scratcher:** this narrow-bristled wire brush helps you uncap the wax cells when getting the honey out or checking for disease.

As a beginner, you are best buying ready-made hives. Later, you can buy kits if you want to expand.

Placing the Hive

This depends on property size, how near your neighbors are, access, landscaping, etc. Bees are pretty flexible, so choose somewhere that lessens the risk of disturbance, etc., your neighbors, you, and your livestock:

- Face the hive entrance south or southeast. Your hive needs at least 6 to 8 hours of sun from early morning.
- To provide the bees with a clean way to and from the hive, ensure that there's a clear path of about a 10- to 15-foot area in front of the hive.
- It's essential to create a fence around the hive to keep any predators at bay.
- Find an ideal location where there won't be any disturbances.
- Use cinder blocks or a proper hive stand so the hive is 12 to 18 inches off the ground. This keeps skunks and other animals out of the hive.
- Weight the hive lid down with a large rock to stop the wind from blowing it off or animals from getting into it.

Get Your Bees

Beekeeping firms, local beekeeping associations, and farm supply organizations all offer online ordering for bees. You will have to inquire about ordering and delivery schedules from nearby companies. Orders are typically placed in January and delivered in March or April.

Ask local keepers if they can recommend reputable sources, and when you find a supplier, ask whether the bees have been treated with antibiotics. You don't want to purchase those because the bees may have American foulbrood disease, which can wipe out your colony.

The most common bees are Carniolan, Russian, and Italian, each with advantages and disadvantages.

- **Carniolan:** these are quiet, gentle bees who spend their winters with low numbers of bees, building up very quickly in the spring. However, they are prone to swarming if they don't have enough room to expand. They are less likely to suffer disease and are excellent at keeping their hives clean.

- **Italian:** You'll find that Italian bees are less defensive than other species and are the most widely preserved and dominant bee race, particularly in North America. They don't abuse propolis, the resinous glue that bees use in their hives, they don't swarm frequently, and they weather the winters well. They do over-brood, too, and they go through honey fast.

- **Russian:** Russian and Italian bees are similar, but Russian bees tolerate varroa mites better. They wait until pollen is available before they raise their broods and stop when the pollen begins to disappear. They also keep a queen cell active all year.

Bees can be bought in two different forms: as a package (bee box) or as a nuc (nucleus colony). The latter are about the size of a shoe box, with a single queen kept in a separate queen box, and are typically constructed of wood, plastic, or screening. They often arrive with enough sugar water to last them for a few days, but they can't stay in the box longer than four or six days after they were placed inside. Nucs offer a significant benefit over bee boxes since they often contain frames with honey and wax, a few bees and their offspring, and the queen.

Be aware that both types can come with diseases, and there will usually be varroa mites. Carefully inspect the bees for anything odd before you introduce them to your hives.

Install the Bees

1. Choose a sunny, warm day, above 55°F, with no wind if possible.
2. Give your bees a 1:1 sugar-water solution. Remove a frame from the hive and install an inline feeder if you have one. Place your

Boardman feeder at the hive's entrance if you have one.

3. From the feeder, you can transport three or four frames.

4. Get dressed in your bee suit, hat, veil, gloves, and boots.

5. Using a mix of water and sugar, spray the box. This will simultaneously feed the bees and help them calm down.

6. Open the bee box and remove the sugar can, leaving the queen undisturbed.

7. Take out the queen box, clear the worker bees from it, and set it above the frames. To keep the other bees where they are, replace the sugar can.

8. Insert the queen into the colony. Ascertain that she is not facing the box's corked end, then carefully take the cork out. Put a tiny marshmallow into the hole as soon as possible. The queen will be released for the following several days as the remaining bees gnaw into it. By doing this, they ensure that they perceive the queen as their queen by imprinting with her pheromones.

9. Using an elastic band or stapler, suspend the queen box between the two middle frames. The screen of the queen box should not be covered in any way. To feed the queen, the bees must have access to her via the screen.

10. After the queen is inside, shake the bees into the hive and take the sugar can out of the bee box. To get as many out as you can, do this firmly.

11. Replace the frames slowly, making sure all the bees are out of the way so they don't get injured or killed.

12. To ensure that any bees that are left leave and head towards the queen, you can place the bee box inside the entrance to the hive.

13. Now, place the inner and top covers on.

14. Weight the top down, find the smallest opening and install the hive reducer.

You have to spend as much time as possible outside the hive over the following few days. The bees can turn on the queen and obtain a new one if they are agitated excessively during the settling process. Seeing dead bees emerge from the front entrance is one of the best indicators that your hive is settling. This indicates that the worker bees have made their home and are tidying the hive.

Open the hive a few days after installation and ensure the queen has been let out. If yes, the queen box can come out. If not, quickly open the box and get it back into the hive. Replace the inner and top covers to stop her flying away.

Within 7 to 10 days, you can look at the frames and see if the queen is laying eggs.

- You should check on the hive every 10 to 21 days.
- Make sure your beekeeping equipment is kept clean to stop diseases and pests from spreading.
- Place a shallow birdbath or dish for water near the hive and keep it filled. Make sure the bees cannot drown in it.
- Fill your garden with flowers and flowering plants so the bees can collect the pollen and nectar. This helps them grow and reproduce healthily, so plant plenty of flowers that bloom at different heights and times throughout the season.
- Keep a close eye on your hive and monitor for diseases and pests that can decimate the hive.

Bee Products

Most people assume that bees only make honey, but, in actual fact, they make many other products, some of them incredibly valuable. Here's what you could get from your beehives:

Honey

Honey is quite complex and is made when honey bees collect sweet deposits and nectar from trees and plants, modifying it and storing it in honeycombs in the hive. This is a great food source for your bees, but you can also gather it yourself, as long as you only take what you need and leave enough in the hive for the bees to feed on.

Nectar

Nectar has a high level of sucrose and comes from nectaries, which are plant glands. It also has a high moisture level, and the bees use that moisture in their honey production process. Nectar is one of the most common sources from which bees get energy.

Beeswax

Beeswax is one of the purest forms of wax and is all-natural. Bees must visit more than 30 million flowers and consume 8 to 10 lb. of honey to make just one pound of beeswax. To do this, the young bees in the colony get together in a large cluster to make their body temperatures rise. Beneath their abdomens are wax-producing glands, and these begin to secrete wax slivers no bigger than a pinhead. The worker bees take these wax slivers and transport them to where they are needed in the hive to form the honeycomb. Each bee will produce around 8 slivers of wax in 12 hours, so you can see the colony's level of patience in building their comb to keep their young safe and fed.

Pollen

Only worker bees have a "pollen basket" in which they gather pollen from flowers and take it to the hive. The pollen is an excellent protein source for bees to raise a healthy brood. Sometimes, excess pollen may be harvested and used as a health supplement. It can be consumed in small amounts, such as sprinkled on a yogurt. If you need to hand pollinate flowers, you can also use the excess pollen, but be aware that it has to be used within a few hours of being collected, or its potency decreases rapidly.

Bee Bread

Bees make this from honey and plant pollen formed into granules and stored within the honeycomb. Bee bread is commonly consumed to stop allergies from pollen, and Olympic athletes also consume it to boost their immune system, recover quickly after a training session, and boost their performance. It isn't recommended that you try to get this from your hive, though. Leave it for the bees to feed on.

Propolis

The word is Greek in origin and translates loosely to "defending the city." Otherwise known as bee glue, bees make it from tree balsams, saps, and resins, and it is often used to seal up any cracks appearing in the hive. If wild bees swarm into a tree hollow, they may even use the propolis to make a way into the hive. Dwarf honey bees coat the branch where their nest is in propolis to stop ants from getting to it, too. Propolis has medicinal qualities and is often taken as a health supplement in capsule form. You might even find it in some toothpaste and cosmetics.

Royal Jelly

This is secreted by honey bees and used to feed their larvae and the queen. Worker bees are the only ones with the hypopharynx glands needed to secrete the jelly. When the workers decide a new queen is needed, usually because the old one has died or is weak, they pick a number of small larvae and place them in cells constructed especially for the purpose. They then feed them on a lot of royal jelly, triggering the larvae into developing "queen morphology," including the ovaries they need to lay the eggs.

All larvae are fed on the jelly, no matter whether they are destined to be workers, drones, or queens. This only happens for three days unless they have been selected as queens. You can harvest royal jelly from your hives if your hive has several queen cells, but only when the queen larvae have reached 4 days old. This is because the queen cells are stocked full of it, whereas the other larvae are fed at certain times. If your hive is managed correctly, you could theoretically collect half a kilo over 5 to 6 months. However, it perishes quickly and must be immediately stored in a freezer or refrigerator until needed or ready to sell.

Bee Venom

Worker bees inject venom when they sting in a bid to protect their colony and themselves. The venom is called apitoxin and is a clear, colorless liquid with proteins that can cause a mild or severe allergic reaction. Bee venom has long been used in natural healing, but collecting it is neither easy nor advisable for those with no experience.

How to Harvest the Honey

The whole point of keeping bees is pollinating your plants and producing honey. The first honey harvest for a new beekeeper is exciting and is actually quite simple, so long as you have the right equipment.

The Right Equipment

Before you start, you need the right equipment, so make sure everything is there first.

The essential tools you will need to harvest a few hives are:
- A hot knife or special uncapping knife to remove the wax caps from the cells.
- A fine strainer to catch debris and dirt in the honey.
- Food-safe buckets to store the honey in before transferring it to jars.
- A tray for the wax cappings – a proper capping tray or a sterilized baking tray.
- Food-safe honey jars with tight lids – plastic or glass will do.

• Measuring jug to transfer the honey to the jars - it must have a spout.

Find Somewhere Suitable

When you have everything together, find somewhere to extract the honey. You can do it outside, but indoors is better as you won't be plagued by bees, wasps, and other insects. Ensure your chosen space is clean and big enough.

Using a Honey Extractor:

1. Make sure your honey is ready to harvest. This means checking that every hive frame is full and the honey is smothered in a white wax cap.

2. Lift the frames and lay them out on a stable surface - make sure it is clean first. Don't take all the honey, as your bees need to feed over the winter.

3. If you have a honey extractor, set it up in the center of your space. Place the mesh strainer on the edge of your bucket and situate it beneath the extractor's spout.

4. Put the capping tray on a bench, plug the knife in, and leave it somewhere stable to heat up.

5. The frames must be uncapped before you can use the extractor to get the honey. Work out how many frames your extractor can hold and remove the wax caps on that many frames. Use the knife to scrape the wax from either side of the frame - do it over a tray, as this can get messy.

6. Fit the frames into the extractor and turn it on or, if it is manual, turn the handle. The extractor tank will spin, and the centrifugal force sucks the honey out, and it drips out through the spout.

7. After a while, check one side of the frame. If it is empty, turn the frame around and repeat to empty the other side.

8. Remove the empty frames, uncap and add more, and repeat until all the frames are empty.

9. It can take an hour or so for all the honey to drain, depending on how many frames you are processing and the heat in the area.

10. During this time, you can sterilize your jars and lids. When the honey is collected, take the collection bucket away, replacing it with another smaller one for any drips.

11. Remove the strainer from the bucket, set it aside, and use your jug to collect the honey and pour it into jars. Tighten the lids firmly, label each jar with the date, and store the honey in a dark, cool place.

Once you have extracted all the honey, you will have a valuable pile of wax that you can use to make other products. However, you will need to remove any traces of honey from the wax. If you have a small amount, you can do this by placing the wax in water and heating it. The wax will float on top of the water, and the honey will stay at the bottom. Once it has melted, let it cool completely and separate the wax from the water. Store it in a clean container with a lid until you are ready to use it. Do NOT use a good pan for this, as beeswax tends to stick, and never use the same pan for anything else. Hopefully, you will be doing this regularly throughout the season, so have a specific pan you use only for this.

Cleaning up is pretty easy, even though honey extraction is messy. However, as honey dissolves in water, simply wash everything with hot, soapy water and clean cloths.

Extracting by Hand:

If you don't have access to an extractor, you can crush and drain the honeycomb to extract the honey. It is an effective method, but it does take time.

1. Remove the frames and break the honeycombs into small chunks. Place them into a food-safe, clean bucket.

2. Using a large masher, crush the comb down, reducing it to a quarter or third of its original volume.

3. Place a large colander over another bucket and pour the crushed honeycomb into it. It will take about an hour to stain through.

4. Next, pour the strained honey through a fine-meshed sieve into another container – you can also line the sieve with cheesecloth if you want. The honey that comes through will be clean and can be transferred straight to the jars and stored.

5. You will be left with the wax, but this can be processed in hot water, as detailed above.

Learn how to make products, such as candles, lip balm, soap, or polish, or use it to waterproof leather, such as horse harnesses, to protect them.

How to Protect Your Bees from Pests and Diseases

Careful monitoring is the best way to stop diseases and pests in your hive. However, that means knowing what to look for and how to deal with them. These are common ones that attack honeybees:

• Aethina tumida

Better known as small hive beetles, these are black-brown and tiny, just ½ a centimeter long. They can travel up to 20 km and quickly infect a hive, causing serious damage to colonies. The beetles are clever, imitating the behavior of the bees so they can enter the hive unharmed. Once in, they lay eggs, which hatch within six days and feed on the pollen, beeswax, and honey, destroying the comb.

Look For:

- Tiny beetles in the comb or hiding in cool parts of the hive
- A rotten-orange smell or slimy combs
- Small eggs in cracks and corners
- Honey fermenting or dripping from the comb cells
- Larvae eating the brood and food stores
- Clumps of larvae in the comb cells or frame corners

Prevention:

You cannot stop these beetles from getting into your hives. All you can do is find them quickly and interrupt their life cycle before they go too far. They are a notifiable pest, so immediately let your local government bee safety and pest management department know.

• Chalkbrood

Caused by a spore-producing fungus called Ascosphaera apis, the bees ingest the spores while they eat, which ferment in the larvae's guts, starving them. Foraging bees usually bring the disease back to the hive, and infection spreads very quickly. Left untreated, it can weaken a hive, allowing other diseases and pests to take hold.

Look For:

- Bee larvae coated in a chalky, cotton-like substance
- Black or grey larvae

- Mummified larvae on the pollen traps or the entrance to the hive
- Brood nests filled with dead larvae

Prevention:

Keep your colony healthy and happy so they can fight off the infection. If the infection has gone too far, you may need to replace the comb frames or re-queen the hive with a much stronger brood.

• Nosemosis

Sometimes called Nosema, this disease is caused by Nosema apis and Nosema ceranae, both single-cell fungi. It is the most common disease in full-grown bees and is incredibly contagious. It can lead to a much shorter lifespan. The spores are ingested through food, cleaning, water spots, and other places in the hive. They go into the stomach, damage the epithelium, and affect the bee's ability to digest.

Look For:

- Worker bees with swollen bellies in the hive
- Fewer bees in the hive or a struggle to survive the winter
- Lack of honey and lower brood populations
- Dysentery

Prevention:

A healthy hive is the best way to prevent this disease, so ensure your bees have the best nutrition. Rotate the hives every few years to keep them strong, and don't move hives when you don't need to keep stress levels low. It is a notifiable disease and must be reported to your region's Department of Agriculture.

• Wasps

The last thing you want is wasps crowding your hives, as they can kill your bees.

Look For: Large groups of wasps

Prevention:

Make the area around the hives unattractive to wasps by growing mint, eucalyptus, citronella, and wormwood. Also, make sure there is no meat or sweet food waste around the hives, as these attract the wasps. Pick up fruit as soon as it falls off the trees, and keep your compost bins and rubbish bins tightly lidded. You can also hang wasp repellants, such as Waspinators, near the hives.

• Wax Moths

Two types of wax moth can attack your hives: Galleria mellonella (greater) and Achroia grisella (lesser.) Both eat larval remains, pollen, and beeswax and will lay their eggs in gaps or cracks. Left alone, they will take over the whole hive.

Look For:
- A broken-down comb.
- Cocoons that look like white webbing.
- Bald parts in the brood.
- Dark feces, shaped like cylinders, on the hive floor.

Prevention:
Again, a healthy, clean hive is the best prevention because strong bees have a better chance of kicking the moths out. Make sure your hive has no gaps, the roof is tight, and that you don't add another entrance, as these are all ways the moths can get in.

• American Foulbrood

AFB is caused by Paenibacillus larvae, a bacterium that forms spores. It can kill bees and entire colonies, even the strongest ones. Spores are spread from hive to hive by infected equipment, and it is incurable. The spores can stay active for at least 50 years.

Look For:
- Patch, irregular patterns in the broods
- Dark, greasy, sunken caps on broods
- Dead larvae – usually a liquid mass
- Decomposing larvae

Prevention:
Follow best practices and keep your equipment clean. Inspect the combs twice yearly, and if an outbreak occurs, the infected hives or colonies must be destroyed, along with infected equipment.

Obviously, the best way to prevent disease and pests is to keep your hives and equipment clean. Build a robust and healthy colony, inspect the hives regularly, and contact pest control if you see anything suspicious.

Ethical and Sustainable Beekeeping

While these are separate concepts, they are interrelated. In beekeeping terms, ethics is about ensuring your bees' welfare and that of their surroundings. Sustainable beekeeping is about keeping the ecosystem healthy and understanding that every action has a consequence.

Ethical Practices:

Ethical beekeeping covers quite a bit of ground, but, in simple terms, it's more about what you don't do rather than what you do. It's about keeping your impact on the bees' lives to a minimum, along with your impact on their natural surroundings. It's also about keeping the bees as stress-free and danger-free as possible while allowing them to go about their lives naturally.

Ethical beekeepers:

- Do not take more from a hive than it can spare
- Only harvest at certain times of the year
- Don't have huge hives, so the bees don't have too much to do
- Don't use chemicals or synthetic replacements for honey
- Keep swarming to a minimum to stop introduced bee species and native fauna from competing for resources

Sustainable Practices:

Sustainable beekeeping is about the relationship between humans, bees, and the entire ecosystem, and beekeepers work to protect the whole bee population, not just their own. Being aware of the environment is important as beekeepers must understand the bees' needs and the dangers they may face.

Sustainable beekeepers:

- Understand the need bees have for a diverse array of flowering plants and will plant different kinds of trees and plants to feed the bees at different times of the year.
- Avoid the use of chemicals, especially pesticides, in their garden, as these can harm the bees.
- Try to keep native rather than introduced species, as the latter can spread disease and cause damage to the ecosystem.
- Adapt their hives to cope with climate change. Bees cannot cope with rapid changes in temperatures, so they ensure the

hives are properly adapted to help them.

Once your hives are set up, keeping bees is relatively simple, and it is an incredibly rewarding part of your homestead. They don't just provide you with honey and beeswax. They also pollinate your crops, ensuring your harvest is a bountiful one.

Chapter 9: Livestock Selection and Care

There will come a time when you'll want to start keeping livestock on your homestead, especially if you want to become more self-sufficient. Most livestock, such as cows, sheep, pigs, ducks, chickens, etc., produce food, and some can even be used to work your land for you.

However, before considering what animals to have, you must prepare your land for them.

Preparing for Livestock

Raising livestock requires a lot of preparation.

https://unsplash.com/photos/brown-goat-on-blue-metal-cage–DdbQGZEkZM

This is the biggest job you will have to do:

- **Shelter and Fencing:** Every animal has its own fencing and shelter requirements, so do your homework first. For example, you can keep chickens in a coop with housing and ventilation, while pigs must be in a secured area, as they are good escape artists. Larger animals, such as cows, need an acre of land per animal.

- **Water:** All animals need water, and large animals can go through several gallons daily. Having a natural, sustainable source of water on your homestead is ideal. Watering your animals in the winter is harder, especially in cold winters where everything freezes solid. To assist with this, you can use electrically heated water buckets and bowls or equip larger troughs with floating heaters. Additionally, be ready to stock up in advance if you use an electric pump to draw water from a well because you might not be able to reach it during storms and power outages.

- **Managing Manure:** keeping livestock means manure and a lot of it, depending on the livestock you keep. However, it can all be used on the homestead. Rabbit manure is a great garden fertilizer, while chicken manure should be added to the compost heap or left to age for a while before using it in the garden. Cattle and horse manure must be left to rot down before using it. Ensure you have an area set aside for manure management on your homestead.

- **Predator Protection:** this is a big problem, especially if your homestead is isolated. In order to protect your cattle and keep the predators away, make sure your fencing and shelters are strong enough to fend off threats from a number of predators, such as wild dogs, hawks, coyotes, and many more.

Choosing Your Livestock

Deciding what livestock you want is also important. There's no point in keeping animals just for the sake of it because that could be an expensive mistake. Here are some of the animals you could consider keeping:

- **Chickens:** The most common livestock or homesteaders, chickens produce eggs, meat, and manure, and you can use them to clear patches of land of insects and weeds.

- **Ducks:** One of the easiest fowl to keep, ducks don't need much space and produce meat, eggs, and manure. They need a constant water source and a secure pen as they are slow creatures that predators can easily get. This includes hawks, so make sure the pen has a covered area.
- **Quail:** These are small birds that are good for meat and eggs. One of the cheaper birds to keep, quails need little space, but be aware that the eggs are small, and you won't get much meat – you might need a lot of them. They are also temperamental layers and, as they are good flyers, they won't be suitable for a free-range homestead.
- **Pheasant:** Larger birds that produce meat and eggs but not in the same quantities as ducks and chickens. They are harder to tame, though, so they may be more challenging, and their laying is irregular.
- **Turkeys:** Larger birds that supply meat and eggs but do need a fair amount of space, especially if you intend to free-range them. They also need a water source and secure pen and shelter.
- **Geese:** Many homesteaders keep geese for their meat and eggs, but also because they make excellent guard animals. They can be vicious, though, and you should have warning signs up if you intend to let them roam your property.
- **Rabbits:** These are an excellent source of meat and breed well, so you can have a steady supply. You should have one male and several females, but be aware they will fight, so be prepared to keep them separate.
- **Goats:** Good for beginners, goats are relatively easy to keep and an excellent source of milk and meat. Do your homework on what breeds to keep, as some are better than others. They are cheap to buy but need a good, secure shelter as they can cause destruction. They also need a regular food and water supply and are escape artists.
- **Pigs:** Another escape artist animal, pigs are quite easy to keep, so long as you keep them in secure pens. Because of their quick reproductive cycle, a piglet bought in the spring is prepared for butchering in the fall. All they really need is a little area, some cover, and water, and they'll eat almost anything.

- **Cows:** If you have plenty of space, cows are not a bad option, but you need secure fencing and pastures to rotate the animals around. Keep in mind you need an acre per animal, and they need a never-ending water supply. If you intend to keep them through winter, they need a lot of care but are an excellent source of milk and meat.

- **Horses:** These are not typical homestead animals because they don't produce food. However, they are good workers and can be used to plow your land, carry goods, and move stuff around your homestead, and they produce plenty of manure. However, they are not cheap to keep and require daily grooming, plenty of water, and a good shelter, not to mention strong fences.

Non-Traditional Livestock

Once your homestead is established, you may want to consider keeping more exotic animals. However, you must be aware that, as these are not local to your area, they are more expensive to purchase and need a lot of care. Some of the commonly kept are:

- **Ostrich:** Excellent source of eggs, meat, and feathers, but they need a lot of space and can be dangerous.

- **Emu:** This animal is smaller in size than the ostrich and provides a decent amount of eggs, feathers, and meat.

- **Llama:** The llama is famously known for its coat of fur. It is used for a number of things, such as carpeting, fabric, and even rope.

- **Alpaca:** The alpaca's fur is also useful as it can be utilized for soft fleece and clothes.

- **Elk:** Large animals that need a lot of space but are an excellent source of meat and fur. However, they are quite dangerous.

- **Bison:** Raised for their meat and fur and are easier to look after than cattle.

Before You Buy

Some animals may look cute, but they are not always easy to care for, not to mention the expense of purchasing and caring for them. Consider a few things before you decide to go down this route:

- Are you eager to have an animal that can be useful for a number of things or even as just a pet?

- Do you think you have the heart to butcher your animals even after raising them?
- Have you ever raised animals for meat before?

Answering these questions will help you determine whether you are ready to keep productive livestock and which breeds to go for. It will also help you determine the type of shelter and fencing you need.

There are some other important questions you need to consider:

- **Can I Keep Animals in My Area?** Some areas don't allow livestock, while others will have rules on what you can and can't keep. Check your local restrictions and requirements before you purchase livestock.

- **Have I Got the Space?** Some animals need more space to roam and live. Consider bees, chickens, and rabbits if you only have a small piece of land. If you have more space, you can consider larger animals.

- **Am I Away from Home a lot?** They may be there for food, but livestock depends on you for everything. If you need to travel, ensure you have someone reliable and knowledgeable who can look after things in your absence.

- **Are They Productive?** You need animals that produce food or other products for a self-sufficient homestead. If they don't, they should be useful in other ways, such as a dog guarding the animals, horses for plowing and as transport, etc. When you look after the animal, you should get something in return.

- **Can I Eat Them?** Not everybody relishes the thought of eating animals they've raised, much less doing the butchering themselves. If that's you, choose animals you can raise for milk and eggs instead. However, you should consider meat animals and, if you can't do the butchering yourself, learn how or find someone who can do it for you.

- **Does the Climate Suit Them?** Most animals will adapt to their surroundings and climate, but not all are suited to certain environments. It's imperative to pick breeds that thrive in the climate you live in.

Legal Considerations

You just need to obtain general liability insurance if your homestead is operated exclusively for you and your family. An EIN (Employee

Identification Number), which is required for anyone selling goods or services, is necessary if you plan to sell any things.

However, the authorities would view your homestead as a commercial company if it is set up to sell products like honey, eggs, and vegetables. This implies that you need to incorporate your company. Additionally, you'll require appropriate homesteading contracts and a website.

If you have livestock, things get a little trickier. You are liable if your animals escape and cause an accident or damage any other property besides your own. You have a legal requirement to provide secure fencing so your livestock cannot escape and also to protect other people from being harmed by your livestock. This doesn't just mean having good fences and locked gates. It also means having plenty of clear signs around the property to warn people of the dangers. You should also consider proper liability insurance in case anyone makes a claim against you for damage or injury.

Building a Shelter

Various livestock shelters exist, and what you need depends on your animals. Before you build, consider the environment and where you want to build it. Then, consider whether the animal will be safe and comfortable.

Ensure your buildings are strong enough to withstand inclement weather like snow, strong winds, or heavy rain. Ensure it has a sloped roof so that snow and rain can run off, and have a water collection or diversion system so the ground doesn't get excessively boggy. Lastly, ensure it has plenty of ventilation.

Three common types of shelter are:

- **Barns:** one of the more popular shelters, barns work well for large animals. They are typically constructed of metal or wood, with a pitched roof, providing space, stalls, tack rooms, feeding areas, and anything else your animals need.
- **Run-in Sheds:** these work well for small herds of sheep or cows and are constructed with wooden walls and corrugated roofs.
- **Tilt Shelters:** these work best in areas that get strong winds. They have pitched roofs and are designed to bend without breaking.

Build or Buy?

If you choose to build, you need time, resources, and help. It isn't easy to build a shelter if you don't know what to do. New homesteaders may find it easier to purchase prefab shelters. However, before you build or buy, ensure your zoning laws allow them.

Materials

If you build from scratch, you will need certain materials. Flooring should be made from concrete as this is easier to keep clean. The main skeleton can be constructed from concrete blocks or solid wooden posts, so long as they go at least a foot into the ground to provide stability and stop animals from knocking them over.

Roofing can be made from tin or corrugated metal, and the sides can be constructed from wooden planks, wire fencing, cattle planks, or even bricks if you have the budget. Consider what is best for your animals and climate, but ensure you don't leave any sharp edges or nails sticking out.

Different Designs

You can choose from several designs, depending on your livestock and budget. Most people start with a run-in shed or open-air barn. However, while these can provide shelter, you must consider that your livestock needs protection from the elements and a clean, dry place to feed. If your climate is hot and dry, these shelters can work. However, they are not ideal if you get strong winds, rain, and cold winters. Even in hot climates, you need to consider insect and pest populations.

Enclosed shelters are the better option, but you must ensure adequate ventilation and shade from the sun and rain.

Building Tips:

- Make sure external doors are tightly shut at night to keep predators out.
- For cold nights, you need a heat source to stop your animals from getting too cold or getting ill.
- Ensure adequate ventilation. Windows on opposite walls and roofline openings are good ideas.
- Poultry should have a covered outdoor area to get fresh air and warmth but where they are protected from the sun.
- Ensure your building materials have no sharp edges and that your roofline gaps don't allow other animals to get in and attack your livestock. You can stop this by placing sheets of strong

wire fencing over them.

Supplementing with Feed

It doesn't matter how many acres of pasture you have or how much extra garden veg you have to feed your animals. You still need to supplement with animal feed. Here's a quick guide for the most common homestead livestock:

Chickens:

Chickens don't just produce meat and eggs. They also give you plenty of manure that contains nitrogen and are a great pest control system. They also eat weeds and can till the soil for you.

They have specific nutritional requirements:

- Plenty of fresh, clean water
- Fats
- Proteins
- Carbohydrates
- Minerals
- Vitamins

They are omnivorous, so they eat vegetation and animals. They need room to forage for insects, seeds, and grass, but they do not have teeth, which means they need grit in their diet to help break their food down. They also need specific chicken feed containing the right mix of nutrition for their age.

- **Age 0 to 6 Weeks:** starter feed
- **Age 6 to 14 Weeks:** grower feed
- **Age 14 to 20 Weeks:** developer feed

Layers need a specific layer feed containing a high calcium level to provide strong shells for their eggs. Purchase a feed with a minimum of 2.5 to 3.5% calcium.

Breeders need a specific layer/breeder feed to get optimum nutrition levels.

Geese:

Geese are great lawnmowers and can clean up areas of your land quicker than you can, especially under bushes and trees. They also make good guardians, keep predators away from other livestock, and provide eggs.

Geese are mostly happy to eat whatever they can find, especially the grass, and will also eat cracked corn and wheat grain, vegetables, fruit, and insects. They have serrated edges on their beaks, making them good grazers, but it will hurt if they bite!

For their first 4 weeks, feed goslings on a good starter food with at least 20% protein. Then, they can move to grazing, supplemented with a 16% protein feed.

Cows:

Cows provide milk and meat and are great grazers, keeping long grass down. They produce plenty of good manure to make fertilizer from, rebalancing your soil's carbon levels.

Most of their diet is fresh grass, but they will also eat cut and dried grass (hay) when needed. They also eat corn, oats, and wheat stems and leaves. Beef cows require fats, proteins, carbs, minerals, vitamins, and plenty of water, while dairy cows need food with a dairy meal in it to boost milk production. Dairy cows also need up to 50 gallons of water per day.

Pigs:

Pigs are great for meat production but also work as rototillers on your land. Let them at your land, and they'll till it in no time, digging up rocks, eating roots, and clearing the land of grubs and other insects.

They are omnivorous and will eat many different foods, but you should ensure that 20 to 40% of their food intake is pasture and grain. They will also eat vegetables, fruit, mushrooms, grain, nuts, seeds, insects, and eggs.

They need access to fresh, clean water 24/7 and protein, carbs, minerals, fats, and minerals, all found in an organic, balanced pig feed.

Top Tips for Animal Husbandry

There's more to raising animals than providing food, water, and shelter. For successful animal husbandry, there are certain best practices you should follow:

1. There's No Place for Impulsiveness

This is the first rule of animal husbandry to learn and understand. Never be impulsive in buying or obtaining livestock when you don't have the land or means to care for it properly. Do your homework and take your time. Work out why you want the animals. Do you want chicks because they look cute or because you want the meat and eggs they produce? Are lambs just fluffy, cuddly bundles, or do you visualize the wool and meat they provide? Piglets might be cute, but have you got the space for a full-grown animal or two? What about goats? If you want them for milk and meat, don't buy the first one you see. Research the best breeds for your environment and for the purpose you want them for.

Do you have the money and time needed for proper husbandry? How much money and time are needed for each breed you want to get?

Do you have sufficient space? Can you build a proper shelter and still have enough space for grazing and roaming?

Which types of livestock can you raise together?

Are you prepared to hand-rear young animals if something happens to their mother?

Put simply, know exactly what you want and why, and ensure you can give it the best care possible.

2. Secure Housing

Your livestock must be safe and secure in their new home, giving them somewhere to escape the weather, keep away from predators, and roam about. All animals have specific needs, but you must be realistic. You cannot keep the animals in cramped conditions, as they need to be able to move about freely. Too many animals in too small a space can also lead to illness and disease.

They will need the right kind of shelter, too. Chickens need a coop, goats and sheep need a weatherproofed shed or barn, while cattle and horses need a large barn with plenty of space.

3. Check Your Fences and Check Again

Shelters and space are just one part. Your animals also need secure fencing to keep them in and people and other animals out. What you get depends on your livestock. Chickens will get away with wire fencing as long as they have a secure building to roost in at night. Other animals may need electric fences. Once your fence is up, you must check it daily and immediately make necessary repairs.

4. Water Access

All animals need water, but you don't want to be out there every 5 minutes with buckets. Ensure your animals have constant access to water, especially larger animals who would benefit from a natural water source on the land. You must also be prepared for cold winters, have water stocked up ahead of time, and be ready to thaw water if it freezes solid.

5. The Best Nutrition

Healthy, well-cared-for animals provide healthy food for you, so their nutrition is one of your top priorities. Whether you purchase it or make your own, you must ensure your livestock gets the right nutritional needs and supplement feed where needed.

6. Get a Good Veterinarian

Ensure you do this before you have any livestock because they can help you choose the right ones and give you plenty of advice about their care. You also need to know you can call your vet any time, day or night, should an emergency arise.

7. Think about the Environment

You must consider whether your chosen livestock can handle environmental factors. Some breeds are happy outside, while others aren't. Some animals handle the heat, while others are better suited to colder temperatures and can happily survive a harsh winter with the right care. You also need to consider that you will be looking after them, so ask yourself if you can handle extremes of temperature every single day. This isn't the type of job where you can decide not to go to work because of the weather!

8. Inspect Your Livestock Daily

Successful husbandry takes time and effort. That means checking on all your animals every day. You'll need to understand what issues each breed may face so that you can quickly carry out your inspections. That way, you stand a better chance of picking up on a disease, illness, or injury and dealing with it immediately.

9. Have a Good First Aid Kit

A first aid kit for animal husbandry should contain the following at a minimum:

- A syringe
- Antibacterial/antifungal spray
- Bandages
- Corn starch
- Cotton swabs

- Electrolyte powder
- Gauze
- Hydrogen peroxide
- Neosporin
- Saline solution
- Scissors
- Towels
- Tweezers
- Vaseline

You also need to check with your veterinarian to see if there are specific medications, creams, and ointments you should keep on hand.

10. Be Ready for the Poop

There will be a lot of it, and you must keep your livestock areas clean. Have a plan in place for cleaning it up regularly (at least twice daily) and what you will do with it. Some choose a composting system where the poop can be turned into rich fertilizer. Others heap it up and let it age before spreading it on their land.

No matter what you do, husbandry can only be successful if you keep these tips in mind and be prepared to put in the time and effort. If you are not 100% committed, don't even consider keeping animals.

Sheep Shearing Techniques

If you have sheep and want to harvest their wool, you need to learn how to shear them. You may have some idea how to do it, but if you don't do it properly, you can stress the animal and potentially cause injury to you or it.

Here are some shearing tips to help you:

- **Be Confident:** This is one of the most important things to learn about shearing. Confidence is everything, so never fumble with the shears, and don't second-guess yourself, or you are more likely to go wrong. You should also get into a good rhythm to move easily between the sections that need shearing.

- **Don't Make Second Cuts:** If you don't perform the first cut properly, you are forced to make a second cut. This isn't ideal as these bits can't go onto the rolled fleece, as they weaken the yarn and cause pilling. Experience is the only thing that will teach you how to avoid making second cuts.

- **Keep the Skin Taut with Your Non-Dominant Hand:** This allows the shears to move easily, and you'll cut closer because the skin is stretched. This is important when shearing fine-wooled sheep, as they have wrinkled skin, and it's not so easy to see through the wool.

Know Your Sheep

This helps you shear your sheep better:

- Is she fat or thin? This helps you move the shears at the correct angle for her body shape.
- How many teats? Some have two, while others have four, and you need to know so you can steer clear of them when shearing.
- Is the sheep healthy? If yes, there'll be plenty of lanolin in the wool that melts and makes it easier for the shears to slide through. If not, the lanolin is thick, which makes it difficult to move the shears.

Milking Techniques and Tips

Knowing how to milk your cattle properly is essential to getting a good supply of milk and ensuring your animals are comfortable. Good techniques are also essential to the animal's health.

How to Get Sufficient Milk:

How do you know you are getting as much milk as your cow can give? The answer lies in the animal's health, comfort, and calmness.

- **Health:** you will nearly always get more milk from a healthy cow than an unhealthy one. Check your herd for signs of illness, stress, or disease, and if anything looks wrong, contact your vet. Also, make sure your animals receive their vaccinations.
- **Comfort:** cows need good food and plenty of fresh water, shelter from the elements, and space to roam and graze. If a cow is cold, she shivers, using energy to stay warm. If she is too hot, she won't eat so much. Both result in a lower milk yield.
- **Calmness:** never shout at your cows or hurt them, or they get distressed and scared. That means less milk, so be calm and gentle with them, and you'll get more milk.

Keep Things Clean

You must keep the enclosure, shelter, and milking area clean. If they are dirty and wet, it can lead to disease. The cows must also be kept clean, especially just before you milk them. Brush them down to remove dirt and dust, use warm water to wash their teats and udders gently, and dry them with paper towels.

Cut long hair away from the teats and ensure your fingernails are short and clean. Wash your hands thoroughly before milking, and do not cough or spit anywhere near the milk. Also, ensure you have no open wounds or sores on your hands.

Keep It Regular

Cows get used to a routine, so try to milk them at the same times every day. Even a half-hour deviation can result in less milk and cream.

Check for Mastitis

Place a piece of black nylon stocking over a bucket. The first spurt of milk from each teat should go through this. If the milk is watery or lumpy, the cow likely has mastitis, and you cannot use it. Mark the cow and get her treated immediately. From then on, milk her last.

Milking Technique

There's more to milking than grabbing a teat and squeezing it! Following the right technique ensures your cows are comfortable and you get the optimum amount of milk.

1. Lubricate your hands and hold the top of the teat with your thumb and forefinger. Slide them down the teat gently, but do not pull on it. This technique is only for the first milk spurt and is called "stripping."

2. Now, use your whole hand to enclose the teat, keeping the forefinger and thumb around the top. Starting at the top, squeeze each finger on the teat individually, then release the forefinger and thumb and repeat. This is called "expressing" and mimics how a calf feeds from the cow. If your cow is not in calf, take all the milk, or the cow will be uncomfortable.

3. Repeat the first step to get the last spurt when you have all the milk from the udder. Do not tug the teat, as this can cause mastitis, which isn't comfortable for the cow. You should also never use your fingers and thumbs to squeeze out the milk, as this is uncomfortable, damages the top bit of the teat, and can cut

milk production.

4.   When you have finished milking and transferred the milk to a suitable container, wash the milk can and bucket with cold water, followed by boiling water with sodium carbonate dissolved in it – use ½ a cup for every 10 liters of water. Drip-dry them upside down, wash all the cloths in soapy water, and rinse and let them dry.

5 Beginner's Butchering Tips

It won't be easy to do if you have never butchered an animal before. Ensure you learn how to do it properly if you don't intend to let someone else do it.

1. Use the Right Tools

At the very least, you need a *honing steel* to help you keep your knife blades sharp while butchering. It's a given that you will hit the bone occasionally, and keeping a steel nearby allows you to keep the blade sharp.

Next, you need a meat hook. This allows you a good grip when you are separating the meat. You will also need a boning knife, preferably with a well-made steel blade that is semi-flexible.

Next is a machete to cut through big bits and a hand saw to get through the bone. A larger hand saw is also ideal to help you slice larger cuts.

You will also need a tough glove – consider chain mail – to save your hands from the inevitable nicks and cuts.

2. Decide on Your Cuts

Are you after steak? Roasts? Ribs? Or maybe you want hamburgers or stewing meat. Choose the cuts you want and research how to make those cuts. The best place to go is a butcher, as they can tell you or even give you a visual guide on each cut. Knowing how to make your cuts will give you a good idea of how to process the meat. Once you have the cuts you want, you can use the rest of the carcass to make exploratory cuts and learn from your mistakes. You can turn scraps into stewing or ground meat, so there won't be any waste. However, try not to turn the loin meat into scrap. This is the bit on the top of the spine and is classed as high-value meat.

3. Learn to Be Organized

Make sure you have enough space to process the meat. Several buckets and a way of labeling each cut is also recommended. You can tack bits of paper to them if you like. Once you've processed enough animals, you'll learn what each cut looks like, thus speeding up the process.

4. No Two People Process the Same Way

That means that no one process is better than any other. When you have an entire carcass, you can afford to make a mistake or two, and you'll learn your own process along the way. So long as you know where the cuts come from, you'll find a comfortable way of processing that makes sense to you.

5. Control the Carcass Temperature

This can make all the difference in how you process the meat. It will be much harder to cut and take forever if it is too cold, even partly frozen. If your meat is frozen before you process it, let it thaw for 24 hours in a warmer room – not too warm, though. Some meat, especially beef, is left to hang for at least 18 to 21 days to ensure it is tender enough. If the meat is warmer, it will be easier and faster to process, and peeling the muscles back and finding the joints is also easier. Never try to process a frozen carcass, as it will take too much time and won't do your hands any favors, either.

Five Tips for Raising Livestock for Food

You may not make much profit when you raise animals for food, but it gives you the highest-quality meat and can save you money in the long run. You only need enough land per animal, good, healthy feed, plenty of water, and time to care for the animal.

As a homesteader, you will probably consider livestock at some point in your journey, especially if you want to be self-sufficient, and at least you will know what went into your food and how the animal was treated. When you purchase meat from a store, it may meet the USDA standards, but you may be shocked to learn how the animals were kept and raised before being slaughtered.

Raising your own animals means knowing they were treated kindly, humanely, and looked after well. You know what it was fed and whether it was healthy. Many homesteads raise cows for milk and beef, raise pigs, egg-laying birds, and meat birds, and there's good reason for doing all of this.

Grocery store prices are rising fast, and most of the meat, eggs, and milk you can buy there comes from animals raised in less-than-ideal conditions. Listen to the news, and most days, you will hear about an outbreak of one disease or another, affecting prices and food quality, so it's little wonder that more people are raising their own food supplies.

Make no mistake, though. Raising your own livestock for food is not easy. It takes time, money, effort, and a lot of blood, sweat, and tears, but the rewards are huge. Humans have been doing this for centuries, and, in many places, it is a way of life. Homesteading is about going some way toward making it a way of life for you.

Here are some tips to help you make the best of it.

Choose Your Livestock with Care

You have several options if you decide to raise animals for meat:

- **Meat Chickens:** Ready to butcher at eight weeks old.
- **Laying Hens:** Some breeds can be used for eggs and meat. If you buy hens, you have an instant source of meat.
- **Beef Cattle:** You need an acre per cow for grass-fed, but you'll get enough meat from one cow to last an entire year.
- **Pigs:** Must be fenced in, but you'll get a decent amount of meat if you put in the effort for 6 months. They will eat any food scraps from your garden, but you will likely have to purchase a supplemental feed.
- **Sheep:** Easy to raise, so long as they have plenty of pasture land to graze on, and you'll get a decent amount of meat. Be aware that mutton takes more cooking than lamb.
- **Goats:** Goats don't need to graze on high-quality pasture land and are easy to keep. They produce a decent amount of meat, but it must be cooked long and slowly, or it will be quite tough. Kid meat is more tender, but you don't get so much of it.
- **Rabbits:** Ready for butchering from 8 weeks old, and as they breed so well, you get a plentiful supply.

Think about the Endgame

If you can't decide what animals to raise, think about what you want. Knowing your endgame will tell you what animals you need. If you want a small dairy farm, start with goats or cows. You'll need a beef cow if you only want or have space for one animal but want a lot of meat. If you want a quick way of getting meat on the table, you'll want rabbits and meat chickens, as both can be butchered at eight weeks.

Consider the Expense

You know that raising livestock isn't free, nor will it be cheap. You have the initial layout of purchasing the animals, building shelters, fencing, and then there's feed, which is an ongoing purchase. You may be forgiven for thinking it must be cheaper just to go buy your meat from the store.

Raising some animals will be cheaper if you have plenty of grassland, especially cattle, but you need enough for them to graze from spring through to fall. You will have to purchase haylage (fermented grass) to supplement during the winter, but this is much cheaper than bales of grass. However, if you don't have enough land, you need to consider the cost of buying food.

Young chicks and piglets need a heat lamp in the colder days, but cattle, goats, and sheep tend to be easier. So long as they have shelter, they can keep out of the wind and rain and are reasonably self-sufficient.

You will need to consider the cost of repairs to your fences and shelters, another ongoing cost. In terms of breeding for succession, see if you can come to a deal with a neighbor who may have a bull, a billy goat, a ram, or other male animals that you can breed yours with.

Weighing up all the costs, work out the cost per pound of raising your own against purchasing from a store. Also, consider that your own animals are likely to be raised organically, whereas you cannot guarantee that with store-bought meat.

If you find feed and butchering too expensive, see if you can go halves with a neighbor. Food bought in bulk is generally cheaper, too. If you live in a homestead or farming area, you'll find plenty of people willing to help out and share costs.

Consider the Time

Raising livestock is not a 5-minute job. You need to be committed big time because your animals will need daily care. Even if they graze during the summer, you must provide fresh water regularly. You could consider an automatic stock tank valve. This ensures your water tanks stay full without you needing to fill them. Large animals drink an awful lot of water in a day, and it's a tough job if you have to keep trenching out to the field to top it up.

You also need to inspect your animals every day for signs of stress, disease, illness, and injury. You must keep an eye on your fences and ensure any damage is repaired straight away, and this has to be done regularly.

If you have to go away, you need to hire someone who is capable and knowledgeable to care for your livestock, and regardless of the weather, whether you are ill or if anything comes up, you still need to get out there and tend to those animals.

Think about the Emotional Investment

Livestock are not pets. Yes, you will look after them and get to know every one of them, but you must keep telling yourself that they are food, not pets. You must learn to distance yourself emotionally while still providing a clean, safe environment that's as close to their natural habitat as possible. That means raising them organically, grass-fed, and pasture-raised.

You will benefit from knowing that your animals are happy and healthy. Stressed animals translate to tough meat, while happy animals are tastier and better for you.

Raising livestock is well worth the effort, provided you have the time and money to do it.

Chapter 10: Making Your Own Dairy and Meat-Based Food

It doesn't matter whether your homestead is a tenth of an acre or a hundred because you can be self-sufficient in many ways. By definition, homesteading is all about self-sufficiency and sustainability. It's about growing your own food, raising livestock for food, preserving your food to keep it for longer, and may even involve making your own clothes. It means living within your means and doing your bit to fight climate change.

Growing veggies can be done small-scale in containers and raised beds or large-scale with huge fields of food, and you can preserve it in many ways to keep your family fed the whole year. In the same way, you can raise enough livestock to feed your family without relying on grocery stores for meat, dairy, fish, etc., that you know is not organic and has often been raised in poor conditions. When you raise animals for eggs, meat, and dairy, you have everything you need to survive on your journey to self-sufficiency.

Humans started life as hunter-gatherers, fishing and hunting for food to sustain them. Being a homesteader means you are getting back to basics, learning how to provide your family with good, nutritious, organic food in a sustainable lifestyle that helps you, your community, and the climate.

Let's look at how to process and preserve some of the meat and dairy you have raised on your homestead.

Handling and Processing Dairy

How to Handle Raw Milk

There has been much scaremongering about raw milk, but it is incredibly safe and clean. It only becomes unsafe when it comes into contact with contaminated containers, surfaces, and tools.

When handling raw milk, you must ensure you sterilize everything it may come into contact with, including your hands!

Storing Raw Milk

Your storage system must be in place before you get your dairy animals. Each cow can produce up to 35 liters of milk daily, and if you have nowhere to store it, you'll waste it or spend a ton of time turning it into something else – every day!

Raw milk will stay fresh for up to two weeks when properly refrigerated.
https://unsplash.com/photos/mason-jar-filled-with-smoothie-S1HuosAnX-Y

Milk will stay fresh and sweet for up to 2 weeks when properly refrigerated. After that, you can still culture or use it in baking, but it won't taste so nice when you drink it.

Using Your Milk

No matter what dairy product you see at the store, there's a pretty good chance you can make it at home. Here are some simple recipes to get you started.

Queso Blanco Cheese

This is one of the easiest cheeses to make and has a lovely, mild flavor.

Ingredients:

- 1 gallon of milk.
- ¼ cup apple cider vinegar.

Instructions:

1. Heat the milk to 185 to 190°F, stirring to stop it from burning.
2. Remove it from the heat when it gets to temperature, and stir in the apple cider vinegar a bit at a time, stirring until the curds and whey have separated.
3. Put the curds in a cheesecloth and hang them for a couple of hours until no more liquid drips out and the cheese has solidified and cooled.
4. Slice, crumble, or cube, and enjoy within a few days.

Yogurt

Ingredients:

- 1 small tub of plain, active yogurt.
- A quart of milk

Instructions:

1. Heat the milk until bubbling. You should see skin forming on the top.
2. Pour it into a quart glass jar and leave it to cool down to about 115°F.
3. Stir in 2 to 3 tbsp. of plain yogurt and stand the jar in a pan. Add hot water from the tap (as hot as possible) until it reaches the yogurt level.
4. Leave it to set for 8 to 12 hours, and then cool it in the fridge.

In the future, use a little of this as your starter in the next batch instead of buying it.

Sour Cream
Ingredients:

- 1-quart milk
- 1 pack sour cream starter

Instructions:

1. Heat the milk gently to 86°F. If it's a hot day, pour it into a jar and set it in the sun until it warms up.
2. Add the starter and shake or stir it.
3. Leave it at room temperature to thicken up to 24 hours.
4. Label it, and refrigerate.

Butter
Ingredients:

- 2 cups heavy cream off the milk.
- ½ tsp. salt

Instructions:

1. Use an electric mixer to mix the cream and salt on speed 8 or 9. Mix for 10 to 15 minutes until the bowl is coated in solids.
2. Scoop the solids into a ball and hold it under cold running water, squeezing it until the water runs clear.
3. Simply store it in the refrigerator and use it within a few weeks.

The liquid left in the mixing ball is buttermilk, which you can use in baking.

Handling and Processing Meat

When you handle raw meat, you must wash your hands thoroughly before and after to avoid cross-contamination, and never use the same equipment you used on meat with any other food.

There are a couple of ways to process meat, the most popular being curing.

Curing Meat

You can do this in two ways. The first method is salt curing, and the second is brining, typically used for food smoking. For example, you would need 2 to 3 tbsp. of salt to cure a 5 lb. steak, although sometimes sugar is used too, but that depends on the recipe.

Brining can also preserve, ferment, and pickle meat, enhancing the flavor, color, and texture. Highly salted water is usually used in brining. If you have a 15 lb. joint of meat to brine, submerge it in just enough water to cover it and stir in 6 tbsp. of salt. As soon as the meat has soaked in the brine all through, it can be smoked until tender.

Brining and curing are the secrets to perfectly smoked meat, imbuing it with a smoky flavor that keeps it tender and moist. The trick is not to put too much meat in the container to ensure plenty of room to absorb the brine or salt completely.

If you don't have access to a smoker, there are a couple of other ways to use up some of your meat apart from freezing it.

Homemade Sausage

Ingredients:

- 3 ½ lb. lean meat – whatever you have available
- 1 ½ lb. fatty meat – pork belly, shoulder, etc.
- 2 tbsp. kosher sea salt
- 1 tbsp. black pepper
- ½ cup ice water
- Sausage casings

You will also need a meat grinder and a sausage stuffer

Instructions:

1. Chop all the meat and fat into small chunks – they must fit the grinder.
2. Put them in a bowl, mix with the salt, and refrigerate overnight.
3. The next day, freeze your blade, auger, and dies for an hour and soak 15 feet of sausage casings in warm water.
4. Mix the meat chunks with the black pepper and grind them using a coarse die. If the meat is still below 38°F, you can grind it again using a fine die. If not, freeze it for 20 minutes and grind it again.
5. Freeze the meat – it must be as close to freezing as possible. Remove it from the freezer, add the ice water, and work it with your hands for 60 to 90 seconds until you have a sticky ball.
6. At this stage, you can use this as sausage meat or make sausage links. If you want links, put the meatball into the sausage stuffer, slip on the casing, and leave a 4-inch tail.

7. Remove the air by cranking the stuffer down and "milking" the casing out of the tail. Then, fill the casing with the meat. Repeat until you have used all the meat – don't make them too tight.

8. Make the links. Press one end and tie it off, then pinch a link off about 6 inches in. Twist it away from you a couple of times to seal it, then repeat, twisting it towards you this time. Do this down each coil and tie the last one off.

9. Check for air bubbles in the links, using a needle to prick them out, compressing the meat gently to fill in any gaps. Hang the sausages for 24 hours before consuming, freezing, or storing.

Chicken Liver Pate

Ingredients:

- 1 lb. chicken liver
- 1 cup milk of your choice
- ¼ cup unsalted butter
- 1 tbsp. olive oil
- 3 to 4 minced garlic cloves
- 1 cup finely chopped onion
- 2 whole bay leaves
- ½ tsp. dried thyme
- ½ tsp. salt
- ½ tsp. pepper
- ¼ cup brandy

Instructions:

1. Put the liver in a bowl, cover it with milk, and stir gently. Refrigerate for at least 2 hours.

2. Melt the butter and olive oil over medium heat, and cook the onions until soft. Add the minced garlic and cook for a minute or so, but do not allow the onions and garlic to go brown.

3. Add the liver, salt, pepper, and bay leaves and cook until the liver is just a little pink inside and browned all over.

4. Remove from the heat, add the brandy, and place it back on the heat. Set the brandy on fire and cook until the liquid has gone. Remove the bay leaves and let it cool.

5. Once cool, blend to a smooth pate and refrigerate for several hours before eating.
6. This pate also freezes well.

Chapter 11: Preserving Meat, Dairy, and Eggs

Making delicious dishes with meat and dairy is one way to preserve it. However, if you don't want to use it immediately, there are other ways to preserve it for long-term use.

Preserving Meat

Meat can be safely stored for years if it is properly preserved.
https://unsplash.com/photos/sliced-meat-beside-silver-knife-Xcdxbjx7MFg

You can safely store meat for years if you preserve it properly. The obvious way is to freeze it, but there are some other methods you can use, some thousands of years old.

Freezing:

Before freezing meat, it must be prepared to prevent freezer burn and prolong its life.

- Wrap meat and poultry in a couple of layers of plastic wrap, then a layer of aluminum foil and a plastic bag designed for freezer use.
- You can also use a home vacuum sealer to shrink-wrap your meat.
- Airtight plastic or freezer-safe glass containers are also safe to use.
- Do remove as much bone as possible, as these are a contributing factor in freezer burn, and the more bone you store, the less room you have for meat.
- If you want to freeze sliced meat or patties, place a sheet of parchment paper between them to stop them from sticking together.

Label Your Packages

Each package or container must be labeled with the type of meat, date, and whether it is raw or cooked. Try to group items, i.e., all the chicken together, and separate cooked from raw.

Use the meat in date order, i.e., earliest first. That way, you won't waste food that has freezer burn or is out of date.

Know How Long to Store It

Contrary to popular belief, meat cannot be stored in a freezer forever:

- **Uncooked Meat:** chops, steaks, etc. – 4 to 12 months
- **Uncooked Ground Meat:** 3 to 4 months
- **Cooked Meat:** 2 to 3 months
- **Lunch meat, Ham, and Hotdogs:** 1 to 2 months
- **Poultry:** cooked and uncooked can be stored for 3 to 12 months
- **Wild Game:** 8 to 12 months

Ensure your freezer temperature stays at 0°F or lower.

Thaw Your Meat Properly

It is rarely a good idea to cook your meat from frozen. Knowing how to thaw it properly can save you from food-borne illnesses.

- **In the Refrigerator:** Things like full turkeys can take up to 24 hours to thaw, so plan ahead. This is the safest method.
- **In Cold Water:** Ensure the meat is in airtight packaging and submerge it in cold water. The water must be changed every half-hour until the meat is thawed.
- **In the Microwave:** The meat must be cooked immediately afterward, as microwaves are notorious for uneven thawing and can even begin to cook some of the meat.

Check your meat before you cook it. If it smells off or has gone an odd color, discard it.

Salt Preservation:

As mentioned earlier, salt can be used to preserve meat, which is one of the oldest ways.

- Use proper curing salt – you can get this online.
- Meat should be put into airtight bags or containers and covered completely in salt. The best way is to start with a layer of salt, add meat, another salt layer, meat, and so on.
- Containers should be stored at 36 to 40°F for a set time – do not allow them to freeze.
- The formula for how long to cure your meat is seven days for each inch thick. For example, a ham weighing 12 to 14 lb. and 6 inches thick should be cured for 42 days.
- You can keep salt-cured meat for up to four months without refrigeration if you store it in airtight containers or bags.
- Always rinse off excess salt before you cook it.

Dehydration:

Making jerky is an excellent way of making protein-rich snacks and needs only an oven and stovetop or a dehydrator.

- Slice the meat into thin strips with a 1 cm. x 1 cm. cross-section.
- Boil it for 3 to 5 minutes – this removes all bacteria.
- Drain the meat until it has dried.

- Bake for 8 to 12 hours on the lowest setting in your oven, or use a food dehydrator (follow the manufacturer's instructions.)
- When dried properly, the meat will feel leathery, hard, or sticky.

You can store jerky for up to two months in an airtight container without refrigeration.

Smoking:

Smoking is a great way of preserving meat, and it adds flavor.

- Meat should be salt-cured first, as this will allow for longer storage.
- Smoke in a proper smoker for 7 hours at 145°F or 5 hours at 155°F. Do not go over 155°F as the meat will cook rather than be smoked or dried.
- Be aware that some cuts, such as brisket, may take longer, up to a day in some cases.
- A meat thermometer should be used to check the internal temperature before taking the meat from the smoker. Poultry should be 165°F, roasts, steaks, and chops 145°F, and pork and ground meat 160°F.
- Flavor the meat using mesquite, hickory, or cherry wood chips.
- Store for up to 3 months in an airtight container.

Canning:

Canning is another popular method of preserving meat, but the process must be followed exactly for safe preservation.

Always Use the Right Tools:

- Meat should be processed using a pressure canner as the steam sterilizes the meat, cooking it and sealing it in the jars.
- Always use Mason or other good canning jars with no chips or cracks.
- Never open the canner until the processing is complete and it has cooled and naturally depressurized. Do not force it by running cold water over the canner.
- You can store canned meat for up to a year in a cool, dry place.

Canning Poultry/Rabbit:

- **Hot Pack:** Steam, boil, or bake until the meat is two-thirds cooked. Pack it into the jars with 1 tsp of salt in each, adding hot broth and leaving 1 ¼-inch headspace.
- **Raw Pack:** Pack the jars loosely with raw meat and 1 tsp salt, leaving 1 ¼-inch headspace. No liquid is required.
- **Process:** process for about 65 to 90 minutes, adjusting for altitude if needed.

Canning Chopped/Ground Meat:

- Chopped meat should be shaped into balls or patties and cooked until light brown.
- Sauté ground meat without shaping it.
- Drain off any excess fat.
- Fill the jars and add boiling water, tomato sauce, or meat broth up to 1 inch from the top. You can add salt if required.
- Process for 75 to 90 minutes, adjusting for altitude if required.

Chunks, Strips, or Cubes:

- Remove large bones and precook the meat until it is rare.
- Fill the jars, and add boiling water, meat broth, tomato juice, or meat drippings up to an inch from the top.
- Process for up to 75 to 90 minutes, adjusting for altitude if needed.

Preserving Dairy and Eggs

There are a few ways to preserve dairy and eggs, although most people are surprised to learn that eggs can be preserved.

Eggs:

- **Cold Storage:** unwashed eggs can be refrigerated or stored somewhere cold for months, so long as they still have the bloom on.
- **Freezer:** whip the eggs and freeze them in silicon cups or ice cube trays before transferring them to a bag. You can use these for some baking recipes, but they don't work well for scrambled eggs.

- **Liming**: limed eggs will be kept for at least a year. Use an ounce of pickling lime per half-gallon jar, adding a quart of water and whisking it together. Put the eggs in, pointed end down, and tighten on the lid and screw band to stop air from getting in. Store in a dark, cool place.
- **Freeze-Drying**: You'll need a freeze-drier for this. Blend raw eggs and pour them onto the trays. Process per manufacturer's instructions. You can also freeze-dry cooked eggs in the same way. Store in airtight jars somewhere cool, dry, and dark. You can do the same by freezing the eggs on trays in your freezer.

Preserving Milk

Refrigeration is the obvious way to preserve milk, but it will only last a week or two before it is past its best. Other ways include:

- **Culturing**: make yogurt or kefir from it.
- **Cheese**: this is one of the best ways to use and preserve milk. You can make all kinds of cheese, but be aware that soft cheeses won't keep as long as the harder ones.
- **Freeze**: milk can be stored in plastic containers for a few months, but it will lose its texture over time, and fat globules will make it grainy when you thaw it.
- **Freeze-Drying**: use your freeze-drier as you do for the whipped eggs.

Bonus Chapter: Your Homesteading Checklist

Starting a homestead isn't easy, but it is incredibly rewarding. To help you make sure you do everything right, here's a checklist to follow:

STEP	MILESTONES	DONE
Set Your Budget	• Determine how much you can afford to spend on land/property. • Determine additional fees, including taxes. • Factor in building costs, including buildings, waste management, fencing, etc. • Factor in energy costs. • Can you afford to do this? If yes, move on.	

STEP	MILESTONES	DONE
Find the Land	• Do you want to live off-grid? • Find the right piece of land. • Consider the climate, land, labor costs, regulations and laws, location, proximity to amenities, soil quality, utilities, access, etc.	
Build or Renovate	• If there is already a house, consider renovation costs. • If not, consider building costs – DIY, prefab, or hiring a contractor. • You also need to consider extra buildings for storage and animals.	
Waste Management	• Design and build a waste management system to handle wastewater and sewage. Most people opt for a septic tank. • Get the required permits.	
Energy Requirements	• Are you hooked up to the grid, or do you want to off-grid? • Work out your power needs. • Determine whether you want solar, wind, hydropower, or a combination. • Hire the right contractors to ensure the job is done properly and with the required permits.	

STEP	MILESTONES	DONE
Plan your Homestead	• Visualize what you want to do with your homestead. • Draw a plan of your land and determine where your vegetable garden, fruit trees, chickens, beehives, and livestock will go.	
Prepare the land	• Check and amend the soil quality where needed. • Till the land to get it ready for planting, removing rocks and other debris. • If you don't have enough land for an extensive vegetable garden, build raised beds and plan for square-foot gardening.	
Build a Compost Area	• Find a small corner of the land you can use for compost. • Decide between a heap on the ground or a purpose-built compost heap. • Start filling it with weeds, vegetation, cardboard, and some food scraps to get it going.	
Learn to Preserve Food	• Learn about the different types of canning. • Set up a cool room or root cellar to store veggies, fruits, cheese, butter, etc. • Learn how to freeze, dehydrate, smoke, and cure food to preserve it.	

STEP	MILESTONES	DONE
Determine if You Want Livestock	• Have you got space? • Determine what you want to keep. Most poultry, rabbits, and bees don't take up much space. • If you have acres of land, decide if you want larger livestock, like cattle, pigs, goats, etc. • Ensure you can build the relevant shelters and have strong fencing. • Make sure you are allowed to keep livestock in your area. • Be sure you are willing to do what it takes to care for the animals and keep them healthy and happy.	
Find a Community	• Find a homesteader's community and befriend them. • Look local first and reach out to ask questions or get advice. • Join online communities to trade advice and tips.	

Perhaps the most important thing is to have the right mindset. You will fall at the first hurdle if you are not mentally prepared for the long haul. Homesteading isn't easy, and you need a great deal of determination and dedication to succeed, not to mention the hard work that lies ahead. You don't need to do everything in one go. Take it one step at a time, start small, and plan to expand as you go along – a little every year will soon see your homestead build into a thriving place that you really enjoy being in.

Conclusion

Thank you for taking the time to download and read *"Country Living: The Ultimate Guide to Homesteading, Beekeeping, Raising Livestock, and Achieving Self-Sufficiency in the Countryside."* We hope you found it useful and now have a good idea of whether country living or homesteading is the life you want to lead.

Homesteading is what you make of it. You can go all-in and live off-grid completely, or you can simply cut your reliance on public utilities by using some renewable energy and water sources. You can become totally reliant on the food you grow and raise, or you can simply become less reliant on grocery stores.

This is your life. This is you, living the way you want to live, no matter how hard it is to start with. And make no mistake. This is not an easy life, at least not to start with. It will cost you financially but also in blood, sweat, and tears, but the rewards will eventually far outweigh what it costs you, and you'll end up living a life you fully enjoy.

Thank you once again for reading this book, and if you found it enjoyable, please leave a review on Amazon for other potential readers.

Here's another book by Dion Rosser that you might like

References

5 Tips to Raising Livestock for Food. (2015, April 1). Melissa K. Norris. https://melissaknorris.com/tips-to-raising-livestock/

abundantlifehomestead. (2018, June 3). Homemade Baby Food. Abundant Life Homestead. https://abundantlifehomestead.com/homemade-baby-food/

Affordable Ways to Build a House. (n.d.). Www.homesteadfunding.com. https://www.homesteadfunding.com/blogs/affordable-ways-to-build-a-house

Allen, M. (2021, August). The 6 environmental and health benefits of growing your own food. Www.thegardencontinuum.com. https://www.thegardencontinuum.com/blog/the-6-environmental-and-health-benefits-of-growing-your-own-food

Andrews (MA), U. of S. (n.d.). What to Consider When Choosing a Homestead. Treehugger. https://www.treehugger.com/what-consider-choosing-homestead-5111926

Anna. (2019, August 23). Canned Zucchini Spread (Ikra) Recipe. Northern Homestead. https://northernhomestead.com/canned-zucchini-spread-ikra-recipe/

Australia, E. B. S. (n.d.-a). Beekeeping Gear For Beginners. Ecrotek Beekeeping Supplies Australia. https://www.ecrotek.com.au/blogs/articles/beginner-beekeeping-gear

Australia, E. B. S. (n.d.-b). Protecting Your Bees From Diseases And Pests. Ecrotek Beekeeping Supplies Australia. https://www.ecrotek.com.au/blogs/articles/protecting-your-bees-from-diseases-and-pests

Bradley, K. (n.d.). How to Reduce Your Homestead's Carbon Footprint - Grit. Www.grit.com. https://www.grit.com/farm-and-garden/how-to-reduce-your-homesteads-carbon-footprint-zb0z2001/

Burton, L. (2018, December 19). Food Preservation Methods & Guidance. The Hub | High Speed Training. https://www.highspeedtraining.co.uk/hub/food-preservation-methods/

C, C. (n.d.). Winter food storage guide in a root cellar or other cellaring methods – The Home Preserving Bible. http://www.homepreservingbible.com/1057-winter-food-storage-in-a-root-cellar-and-other-preservation-methods/#:~:text=A%20root%20cellar%20is%20an

Choosing the Best Farm Livestock Animals to Raise – Mother Earth News. (2021, April 20). Www.motherearthnews.com. https://www.motherearthnews.com/homesteading-and-livestock/best-farm-livestock-animals-to-raise-zmaz82ndzgoe/

Curing and Smoking Meats for Home Food Preservation. (n.d.). Bradley Smoker USA. https://www.bradleysmoker.com/blogs/articles-smoking-guide/curing-and-smoking-meats-for-home-food-preservation

Dairy Cattle Farming - Raising Cows For Milk. (n.d.). In.virbac.com. https://in.virbac.com/cattle/health-care/dairy-cattle-farming-raising-cows-for-milk

deeannecurtis. (2023, October 13). What to Look for When Buying Land for a Homestead: Key Considerations for Prospective Buyers. https://hummingbird-acres.com/what-to-look-for-when-buying-land-for-a-homestead-key-considerations-for-prospective-buyers/

Dehydrating Food: Is It Good for You? (n.d.). WebMD. https://www.webmd.com/diet/dehydrating-food-good-for-you

Ethical and Sustainable Beekeeping. (2022, October 19). Beeautify. https://beeautify.com.au/blogs/beeautify-blog/ethical-and-sustainable-beekeeping

Extension | Canning Process. (n.d.). Extension.wvu.edu. https://extension.wvu.edu/food-health/home-food-preservation/canning/canning-process

Food Preservation: Making Pickled Products. (2017, November 29). NDSU Agriculture and Extension. https://www.ndsu.edu/agriculture/extension/publications/food-preservation-making-pickled-products

Gardening, E. @ M. (2018, October 1). Small Homestead Layout Design Plans. Misfit Gardening. https://misfitgardening.com/small-homestead-layout-design-plans/

Guidelines for Harvesting Vegetables | Piedmont Master Gardeners. (n.d.). Piedmontmastergardeners.org. https://piedmontmastergardeners.org/article/guidelines-for-harvesting-vegetables/#:~:text=Harvest%20with%20the%20right%20tools

Holte, L. (2021, April 21). 7 Tips for Keeping Happy and Healthy Bees. Miller Manufacturing Company Blog. https://www.miller-mfg.com/blog/7-tips-for-keeping-happy-and-healthy-bees/

Household, I. W. (2022, December 12). The Pros and Cons of Off-Grid Living. Utopia. https://utopia.org/guide/the-pros-and-cons-of-off-grid-living/

How to Assemble A Bee Hive Box or Super - A Beginner Beekeeper's Guide. (n.d.). Beverly Bees. https://www.beverlybees.com/beginner-beekeepers-guide/assemble-bee-hive-box-super/

How to Preserve Meat, Eggs & Dairy. (2021, August 13). Melissa K. Norris. https://melissaknorris.com/podcast/how-to-preserve-meat-eggs-dairy/

How to Reduce, Reuse, and Recycle on the Homestead. (2022, October 7). Homesteading.com. https://homesteading.com/reduce-reuse-recycle-homestead/

How waste reduction can help you have a more sustainable homestead. (2019, April 5). Hello Homestead. https://hellohomestead.com/how-waste-reduction-can-help-you-have-a-more-sustainable-homestead/

https://realestate.usnews.com/real-estate/articles/how-to-choose-the-right-homestead-property. (n.d.).

https://www.cnbc.com/2019/07/02/spending-2-hours-in-nature-per-week-can-make-you-happier-and-healthier.html#:~:text=Those%20who%20spent%20at%20least,nature%20had%20no%20further%20benefits.

Jack, S. (2023, September 27). Homestead Animal Husbandry: 10 Tips for Raising Healthy Livestock. Survival Jack. https://survivaljack.com/2023/09/homestead-animal-husbandry-10-tips-for-raising-healthy-livestock/

Joe. (2020, August 6). Raising Sheep for Wool | Sheep Wool Info. RaisingSheep.net. https://www.raisingsheep.net/raising-sheep-for-wool

June 15, B. D. U., & 2020. (n.d.). How to Dehydrate Fruits and Vegetables for a Healthy Snack. EatingWell. https://www.eatingwell.com/article/290910/how-to-dehydrate-fruits-and-vegetables-for-a-healthy-snack/

Kim. (2018, August 4). How To Start A Vegetable Garden For Beginners. Homestead Acres. https://www.homestead-acres.com/how-to-start-a-vegetable-garden-for-beginners/

Laessig, I. (2019, May 16). How to Make Sprouted Bread. Sunday Supper Movement. https://sundaysuppermovement.com/how-to-make-sprouted-bread/

Magazines, C. (2012, March 27). Milking techniques: the best habits. Farmer's Weekly. https://www.farmersweekly.co.za/farming-basics/how-to-livestock/milking-techniques/

Pallotta, N. (2020, June 7). Vegan strawberry jam. The Plant Based School. https://theplantbasedschool.com/easy-strawberry-jam/

Penn State Extension. (2019, March 13). Let's Preserve: Basics of Home Canning. Penn State Extension. https://extension.psu.edu/lets-preserve-basics-of-home-canning

Pinterest, camp cooking gear to help you enjoy great food in the great outdoors! (2020, May 21). The Ultimate Guide to Dehydrating Food. Fresh off the Grid. https://www.freshoffthegrid.com/dehydrating-food/

RecycleNation. (n.d.). Making Your Own Dairy Products for Beginners – RecycleNation. https://recyclenation.com/2015/07/making-your-own-dairy-products-for-beginners/

Rhodes, J. (2022, September 10). What Farm Animals Eat in a Day. Abundant Permaculture. https://abundantpermaculture.com/what-farm-animals-eat-in-a-day/

Rucker, B. (2022, January 15). How to Build a Shelter for Livestock on Your Homestead | Homesteading Info. Earthineer. https://earthineer.com/animals/how-to-build-a-shelter-for-livestock-on-your-homestead/

Shearing Tips to be a pro. (n.d.). Www.lister-Global.com. https://www.lister-global.com/news/shearingpro/#:~:text=Use%20your%20left%20hand%20to

Spicy Plum and Apple Chutney [Vegan]. (n.d.). One Green Planet. https://www.onegreenplanet.org/vegan-recipe/spicy-plum-and-apple-chutney/

Tamara. (2023, October 6). How to Make Tomato Sauce from Cherry Tomatoes. The Reid Homestead. https://thereidhomestead.com/roasted-tomato-sauce-from-cherry-tomatoes/

The Best Livestock To Raise On A Homestead. (n.d.). Farmer Boy. https://farmerboyag.com/blog/the-best-livestock-to-raise-on-a-homestead/

The Difference Between Pickling and Fermenting. (n.d.). Spicesinc.com. https://spicesinc.com/blogs/difference-between-pickling-and-fermenting#:~:text=An%20easy%20way%20to%20remember

Thomas, C. (2020, August 1). What To Do With Raw Milk + The Anatomy of Raw Milk. Homesteading Family. https://homesteadingfamily.com/what-to-do-with-raw-milk/

Types of Alternative Energy on a Homestead. (n.d.). Survivalist 101. https://survivalist101.com/tutorials/survivalist-homesteading-101/alternative-energy-sources/

University, U. S. (n.d.). Beekeeping | Extension. Extension.usu.edu. https://extension.usu.edu/beekeeping/learn/beginning-beekeeping/index

Printed in the USA
CPSIA information can be obtained
at www.ICGtesting.com
LVHW042017310124
770343LV00002B/14